Illustrator
Barb Lorseyedi

Editors
Evan D. Forbes, M.S. Ed.
Walter Kelly, M.A.

Senior Editor
Sharon Coan, M.S. Ed.

Art Direction
Elayne Roberts

Product Manager
Phil Garcia

Imaging
Rick Chacón

Photo Cover Credit
Images provided by   PhotoDisc
©1994

Research and Contributions
Bobbie Johnson

Publishers
Rachelle Cracchiolo, M.S. Ed.
Mary Dupuy Smith, M.S. Ed.

Hands-On Minds-On Science

Environmental Issues

Intermediate

D1318674

Author
Tricia Ball, M.S. Ed.,
GATE/Mentor Teacher

Teacher Created Materials, Inc.
6421 Industry Way
Westminster, CA 92683
www.teachercreated.com
©1994 Teacher Created Materials, Inc.
Reprinted, 2000
Made in U.S.A.
ISBN-55734-638-0

Table of Contents

Table of Contents *(cont.)*

Introduction

What Is Science?

What is science to children? Is it something that they know is a part of their world? Is it a textbook in the classroom? Is it a tadpole changing into a frog? A sprouting seed, a rainy day, a boiling pot, a turning wheel, a pretty rock, or a moonlit sky? Is science fun and filled with wonder and meaning? What is science to children?

Science offers you and your eager students opportunities to explore the world around you, and make connections between the things you experience. The world becomes your classroom, and you, the teacher, a guide.

Science can, and should, fill children with wonder. It should cause them to be filled with questions and the desire to discover the answers to their questions. And, once they have discovered answers, they should be actively seeking new questions to answer.

The books in this series give you and the students in your classroom the opportunity to learn from the whole of your experience—the sights, sounds, smells, tastes, and touches, as well as what you read, write about, and do. This whole-science approach allows you to experience and understand your world as you explore science concepts and skills together.

What Are Environmental Issues?

All living things depend on the earth's environment to sustain them. People are altering the earth faster and more drastically than any other force of nature. Considering this, an important challenge for us is to learn how to distribute the earth's resources in a responsible way, so that those who need these resources will be able to use them. What can we do to help? Some of the people who work to preserve our environment have a saying that might help us understand. *Think globally, act locally!* Think globally means to understand the complexity of the earth's problems. Learn the history of the earth's bio-systems, which plants and animals rely on these systems, the resources the earth provides, and the people it supports. A deeper look into the past might help us understand the issues of the present. Acting locally is where the fun begins—plant a tree, recycle, reduce, reuse, ride a bike, conserve water. The fun will not stop here; there are many things you can do to preserve the environment. Last but not least, spread the word. Share your knowledge and ideas with everybody interested in listening. Being concerned about the environment should not be a burden; it should be a pleasure we have in taking care of something that is important to us.

The Scientific Method

The "scientific method" is one of several creative and systematic processes for proving or disproving a given question, following an observation. When the "scientific method" is used in the classroom, a basic set of guiding principles and procedures is followed in order to answer a question. However, real world science is often not as rigid as the "scientific method" would have us believe.

This systematic method of problem solving will be described in the paragraphs that follow.

1 Make an OBSERVATION.

The teacher presents a situation, gives a demonstration, or reads background material that interests students and prompts them to ask questions. Or students can make observations and generate questions on their own as they study a topic.

Example: Show students a variety of nonenvironmental cleaning products.

2 Select a QUESTION to investigate.

In order for students to select a question for a scientific investigation, they will have to consider the materials they have or can get, as well as the resources (books, magazines, people,etc.) actually available to them. You can help them make an inventory of their materials and resources, either individually or as a group.

Tell students that in order to successfully investigate the questions they have selected, they must be very clear about what they are asking. Discuss effective questions with your students. Depending upon their level, simplify the question or make it more specific.

Example: What types of hazardous products are in my home?

3 Make a PREDICTION (Hypothesis).

Explain to students that a hypothesis is a good guess about what the answer to a question will probably be. But they do not want to make just any arbitrary guess. Encourage students to predict what they think will happen and why.

In order to formulate a hypothesis, students may have to gather more information through research.

Have students practice making hypotheses with questions you give them. Tell them to pretend they have already done their research. You want them to write each hypothesis so it follows these rules:

1. It is to the point.
2. It tells what will happen, based on what the question asks.
3. It follows the subject/verb relationship of the question.

Example: I think using nonenvironmental products helps contribute to air and water pollution.

The Scientific Method *(cont.)*

4   Develop a **PROCEDURE** to test the hypothesis.

The first thing students must do in developing a procedure (the test plan) is to determine the materials they will need.

They must state exactly what needs to be done in step-by-step order. If they do not place their directions in the right order, or if they leave out a step, it becomes difficult for someone else to follow their directions. A scientist never knows when other scientists will want to try the same experiment to see if they end up with the same results!

Example: We will be comparing environmental against nonenvironmental products.

5   Record the **RESULTS** of the investigation in written and picture form.

The results (data collected) of a scientific investigation are usually expressed two ways—in written form and in picture form. Both are summary statements. The written form reports the results with words. The picture form (often a chart or graph) reports the results so the information can be understood at a glance.

Example: The results of the investigation can be recorded on a data-capture sheet provided (page 43).

6   State a **CONCLUSION** that tells what the results of the investigation mean.

The conclusion is a statement which tells the outcome of the investigation. It is drawn after the student has studied the results of the experiment, and it interprets the results in relation to the stated hypothesis. A conclusion statement may read something like either of the following: "The results show that the hypothesis is supported," or "The results show that the hypothesis is not supported." Then restate the hypothesis if it was supported or revise it if it was not supported.

Example: The hypothesis that stated "using nonenvironmental products helps contribute to air and water pollution" is supported (or not supported).

7   Record **QUESTIONS, OBSERVATIONS,** and **SUGGESTIONS** for future investigations.

Students should be encouraged to reflect on the investigations that they complete. These reflections, like those of professional scientists, may produce questions that will lead to further investigations.

Example: Are all nonenvironmental products toxic?

Science-Process Skills

Even the youngest students blossom in their ability to make sense out of their world and succeed in scientific investigations when they learn and use the science-process skills. These are the tools that help children think and act like professional scientists.

The first five process skills on the list below are the ones that should be emphasized with young children, but all of the skills will be utilized by anyone who is involved in scientific study.

Observing

It is through the process of observation that all information is acquired. That makes this skill the most fundamental of all the process skills. Children have been making observations all their lives, but they need to be made aware of how they can use their senses and prior knowledge to gain as much information as possible from each experience. Teachers can develop this skill in children by asking questions and making statements that encourage precise observations.

Communicating

Humans have developed the ability to use language and symbols which allow them to communicate not only in the "here and now" but also over time and space as well. The accumulation of knowledge in science, as in other fields, is due to this process skill. Even young children should be able to understand the importance of researching others' communications about science and the importance of communicating their own findings in ways that are understandable and useful to others. The environmental issues journal and the data-capture sheets used in this book are two ways to develop this skill.

Comparing

Once observation skills are heightened, students should begin to notice the relationships between things that they are observing. *Comparing* means noticing similarities and differences. By asking how things are alike and different or which is smaller or larger, teachers will encourage children to develop their comparison skills.

Ordering

Other relationships that students should be encouraged to observe are the linear patterns of seriation (order along a continuum: e.g., rough to smooth, large to small, bright to dim, few to many) and sequence (order along a time line or cycle). By ranking graphs, time lines, cyclical and sequence drawings, and by putting many objects in order by a variety of properties, students will grow in their abilities to make precise observations about the order of nature.

Categorizing

When students group or classify objects or events according to logical rationale, they are using the process skill of categorizing. Students begin to use this skill when they group by a single property such as color. As they develop this skill, they will be attending to multiple properties in order to make categorizations; the animal classification system, for example, is one system students can categorize.

Science-Process Skills *(cont.)*

Relating

Relating, which is one of the higher-level process skills, requires student scientists to notice how objects and phenomena interact with one another and the change caused by these interactions. An obvious example of this is the study of chemical reactions.

Inferring

Not all phenomena are directly observable, because they are out of humankind's reach in terms of time, scale, and space. Some scientific knowledge must be logically inferred based on the data that is available. Much of the work of paleontologists, astronomers, and those studying the structure of matter is done by inference.

Applying

Even very young, budding scientists should begin to understand that people have used scientific knowledge in practical ways to change and improve the way we live. It is at this application level that science becomes meaningful for many students.

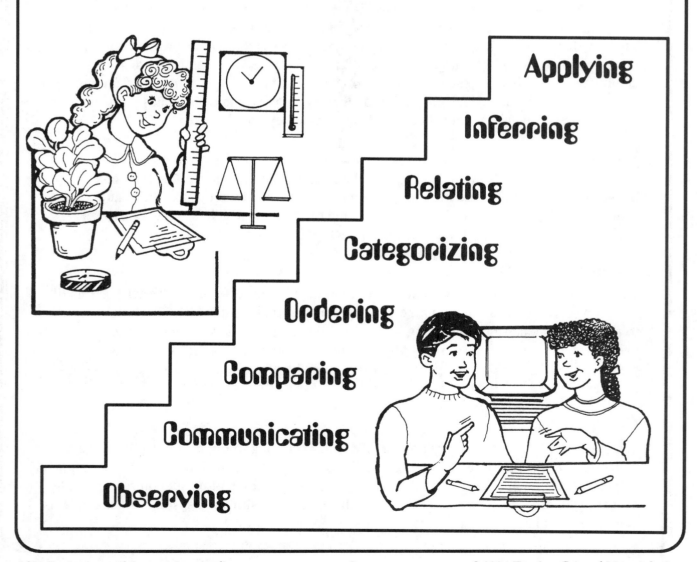

Organizing Your Unit

Designing a Science Lesson

In addition to the lessons presented in this unit, you will want to add lessons of your own, lessons that reflect the unique environment in which you live, as well as the interests of your students. When designing new lessons or revising old ones, try to include the following elements in your planning:

Question

Pose a question to your students that will guide them in the direction of the experience you wish to perform. Encourage all answers, but you want to lead the students towards the experiment you are going to be doing. Remember, there must be an observation before there can be a question. (Refer to The Scientific Method, pages 5-6.)

Setting the Stage

Prepare your students for the lesson. Brainstorm to find out what students already know. Have children review books to discover what is already known about the subject. Invite them to share what they have learned.

Materials Needed for Each Group or Individual

List the materials each group or individual will need for the investigation. Include a data-capture sheet when appropriate.

Procedure

Make sure students know the steps to take to complete the activity. Whenever possible, ask them to determine the procedure. Make use of assigned roles in group work. Create (or have your students create) a data-capture sheet. Ask yourself, "How will my students record and report what they have discovered? Will they tally, measure, draw, or make a checklist? Will they make a graph? Will they need to preserve specimens?" Let students record results orally, using a video or audio tape recorder. For written recording, encourage students to use a variety of paper supplies such as poster board or index cards. It is also important for students to keep a journal of their investigation activities. Journals can be made of lined and unlined paper. Students can design their own covers. The pages can be stapled or be put together with brads or spiral binding.

Extensions

Continue the success of the lesson. Consider which related skills or information you can tie into the lesson, like math, language arts skills, or something being learned in social studies. Make curriculum connections frequently and involve the students in making these connections. Extend the activity, whenever possible, to home investigations.

Closure

Encourage students to think about what they have learned and how the information connects to their own lives. Prepare environmental issues journals using directions on page 82. Provide an ample supply of blank and lined pages for students to use as they complete the Closure activities. Allow time for students to record their thoughts and pictures in their journals.

Organizing Your Unit *(cont.)*

Structuring Student Groups for Scientific Investigations

Using cooperative learning strategies in conjunction with hands-on and discovery learning methods will benefit all the students taking part in the investigation.

Cooperative Learning Strategies

1. In cooperative learning, all group members need to work together to accomplish the task.
2. Cooperative learning groups should be heterogeneous.
3. Cooperative learning activities need to be designed so that each student contributes to the group and individual group members can be assessed on their performance.
4. Cooperative learning teams need to know the social as well as the academic objectives of a lesson.

Cooperative Learning Groups

Groups can be determined many ways for the scientific investigations in your class. Here is one way of forming groups that has proven to be successful in intermediate classrooms.

- **The Expedition Leader**—scientist in charge of reading directions and setting up equipment.
- **The Environmentalist**—scientist in charge of carrying out directions (can be more than one student).
- **The Stenographer**—scientist in charge of recording all of the information.
- **The Transcriber**—scientist who translates notes and communicates findings.

If the groups remain the same for more than one investigation, require each group to vary the people chosen for each job. All group members should get a chance to try each job at least once.

Using Centers for Scientific Investigations

Set up stations for each investigation. To accommodate several groups at a time, stations may be duplicated for the same investigation. Each station should contain directions for the activity, all necessary materials (or a list of materials for investigators to gather), a list of words (a word bank) which students may need for writing and speaking about the experience, and any data-capture sheets or needed materials for recording and reporting data and findings.

Model and demonstrate each of the activities for the whole group. Have directions at each station. During the modeling session, have a student read the directions aloud while the teacher carries out the activity. When all students understand what they must do, let small groups conduct the investigations at the centers. You may wish to have a few groups working at the centers while others are occupied with other activities. In this case, you will want to set up a rotation schedule so all groups have a chance to work at the centers.

Assign each team to a station, and after they complete the task described, help them rotate in a clockwise order to the other stations. If some groups finish earlier than others, be prepared with another unit-related activity to keep students focused on main concepts. After all rotations have been made by all groups, come together as a class to discuss what was learned.

Just the Facts

Anytime two or more persons disagree, you have an issue. People disagree on topics for a variety of reasons. What might some of those reasons be? Think about your bedtime: you and a parent may often disagree on the time you are to go to bed. What is causing the disagreement? Why do you want your bedtime at one time while your parent wants it at another time?

There are many environmental issues. If everyone agreed on how to treat our earth, we would not have any environmental issues. However, different people have different uses, dependencies, and needs for the earth. These needs and values are often a source of disagreement.

Air pollution and water pollution are often in the news today. Think about these issues. See if everyone in your class agrees on the sources and solutions of the problems.

Did you all agree? Probably not. Each of you has the right to your opinion, but think about what causes you to have that opinion. What are the values and beliefs behind that opinion? Who, if anyone, influenced your opinion?

Exploring issues is challenging work. It requires you to think about all the different opinions, sometimes opinions that are opposite of yours. To really understand an issue, you need to get the facts. You need to do some research, surveying, testing, and most importantly...THINKING.

Some sources for help in increasing your understanding of an issue are the following:

- Books, magazines, computer files, encyclopedias, newspapers
- Local, state, and national government officials
- Private organizations concerned about a particular issue
- Concerned citizens
- Corporations

Environmental issues stimulate a wide variety of opinions. Be careful that you do not lump all environmentalists into one group. Many of them have different opinions. If you care about your earth, you are an environmentalist. Sometimes environmentalists are called preservationist—they want to preserve the plants, animals, and land as close to their original status as possible. Other environmentalists are called conservationists—they want to protect the land, plants, water, and animals, but they also think people should be able to use these resources. Can a person be an preservationist on one issue and a conservationist on a different issue?

Issues, Issues, Issues

Question

What is an issue?

Setting the Stage

- Have students think of a disagreement they have had with a parent, teacher, or sibling. What was the issue? What was their position? What was the position of the person they were disagreeing with? How did they express their opinion? Did they resolve their differences?

- Have students share their disagreements in small groups.

- Each student has shared an issue. An issue involves a problem where there are different beliefs and values. For an issue to exist, people must disagree.

Materials Needed for Entire Class

- a large room

- five large signs: one says STRONGLY AGREE the others say STRONGLY DISAGREE, AGREE, DISAGREE, NEUTRAL.

Note to the teacher: The goal of this activity is to help students identify opposing positions on an issue along with the values and beliefs that support a person's position.

Procedure

1. Draw a picture of a spectrum, a line, on the chalkboard. At one end of the line, write Strongly Agree, and on the other, write Strongly Disagree.

2. A spectrum can be used to identify how a person feels about an issue. Ask students to decide where the placement of the following words would be on the spectrum: *agree, disagree, neutral.*

3. Discuss with students the possibility of there being positions between *strongly agree* and *agree, strongly disagree* and *disagree.*

4. Cite these examples to students: Where would you place yourself on the spectrum for these issues?
   - The school day should be longer.
   - Television watching causes violence in our communities.
   - Students living within 1/2 mile of school should be required to walk to school to save gasoline and bus expenses.

5. Point out to students that not everyone agrees.

6. Now clear an area in a large room. At one end of the room, hang the Strongly Agree sign; at the other end, hang the Strongly Disagree. Explain to students that this is a spectrum. Point out about where Disagree, Agree, and Neutral would be. Ask students to stand on the invisible line of the spectrum in response to each of the following statements. (After each statement, ask someone from the five different areas to explain why they chose that position.)

What Are Environmental Issues?

Issues, Issues, Issues *(cont.)*

Procedures *(cont.)*

- Schools should be open year-round with vacations spread throughout the year rather than three months in the summer.
- People should not be allowed to have hand guns.
- Cartoons should have no violent acts in them.
- Sugar-coated cereals should not be marketed.
- The school day should be an hour longer so more learning can take place.

Extensions

- Have students survey newspapers articles on issues where people disagree. Post the articles throughout the unit.
- Have students attend a city council meeting and listen to the issues presented.
- Have students attend a court hearing in their local courthouse. Have them listen to the different points of view. What are the issues?

Closure

In their environmental issues journals, have students pick two statements from the spectrum exercise and write an explanation for why they chose to stand where they did.

A SPECTRUM OF OPINION ON THE ISSUE

Strongly Agree	Agree	Neutral	Disagree	Strongly Disagree

Issues Awareness

Question

What are the environmental issues people are most concerned about?

Setting the Stage

Have students create a concept map of environmental issues. Each time an issue is thought of, think of what other issues are involved related to that issue. Use the outline below for an example.

Materials Needed for Each Individual

- clipboard
- pencil
- calculator
- survey sheets (pages 15-16)
- tally sheet (page 17)
- graph sheet (page 18)
- data-capture sheet (page 19)

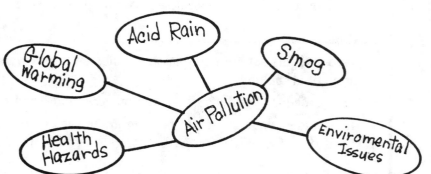

Note to the teacher: In this activity, students will survey ten different people's opinions on the most critical environmental issues facing their community, the country, and the world. They will ask a series of questions and then collate the results.

Procedure

1. Each student will survey ten different people. They should survey five students and five adults. Have each student predict in their environmental issues journal what they think most people will name as the most important issues.
2. Once students have completed the survey, the results will need to be tallied and computed. A tally sheet has been included, or students can make their own. To simplify the process, you may want to ask students to group their answers by the categories listed on the tally sheet.
3. Students should graph their results and answer the questions on their data-capture sheets.

Extensions

- Have students collect copies of *USA Today* newspaper. This paper conducts many surveys, and students can study and interpret the results.
- Invite a sociologist or sociology student to speak to the class about how they use surveys to study human interests and behavior.
- Discuss with students the meaning of values and beliefs. How do values and beliefs influence our opinions on an issue?

Closure

In their environmental issues journals, have students list three examples where someone's values influenced their position on an issue. Have them also list three values a student might have that influence his/her position on an issue. Have them think about the issues spectrum: On what did they base their opinion?

Issues Awareness *(cont.)*

Environmental Issues Survey—Students

Name	What Is the Biggest Environmental Problem Facing Our . . .			Possible Problems
	Community?	**Country?**	**World?**	
1.	Answer: _____ Why? _____	Answer: _____ Why? _____	Answer: _____ Why? _____	1. Air Pollution 2. Water Pollution 3. Population Growth
2.	Answer: _____ Why? _____	Answer: _____ Why? _____	Answer: _____ Why? _____	4. Hazardous Waste 5. Solid Waste/ Recycling 6. Land Use
3.	Answer: _____ Why? _____	Answer: _____ Why? _____	Answer: _____ Why? _____	7. Preserving Open Space 8. Global Warming 9. Endangered Species
4.	Answer: _____ Why? _____	Answer: _____ Why? _____	Answer: _____ Why? _____	10. Acid Rain 11. Rain Forest Loss 12. Energy Consumption
5.	Answer: _____ Why? _____	Answer: _____ Why? _____	Answer: _____ Why? _____	13. Other

Issues Awareness *(cont.)*

Environmental Issues Survey—Adults

Name	What Is the Biggest Environmental Problem Facing Our . . .			Possible Problems
	Community?	**Country?**	**World?**	
1.	Answer: _____ Why? _____	Answer: _____ Why? _____	Answer: _____ Why? _____	1. Air Pollution 2. Water Pollution 3. Population Growth
2.	Answer: _____ Why? _____	Answer: _____ Why? _____	Answer: _____ Why? _____	4. Hazardous Waste 5. Solid Waste/ Recycling 6. Land Use
3.	Answer: _____ Why? _____	Answer: _____ Why? _____	Answer: _____ Why? _____	7. Preserving Open Space 8. Global Warming 9. Endangered Species
4.	Answer: _____ Why? _____	Answer: _____ Why? _____	Answer: _____ Why? _____	10. Acid Rain 11. Rain Forest Loss 12. Energy Consumption
5.	Answer: _____ Why? _____	Answer: _____ Why? _____	Answer: _____ Why? _____	13. Other

Issues Awareness *(cont.)*

Environmental Issues Tally

Number One Environmental Issues			
	Community	**Country**	**World**
Air Pollution			
Water Pollution			
Population Growth			
Hazardous Waste			
Solid Waste/Garbage Disposal/Recycling			
Land Use			
Preserving Open Space/Parks			
Global Warming			
Endangered Species			
Acid Rain			
Destruction of the Rainforest			
Energy Consumption (electricity)			
Other Issues			

Issues Awareness *(cont.)*

Environmental Issues Graph

Mark community, country, and world results in three different colors. Community=Red, Country=Yellow, World=Blue

Graph results for your class.

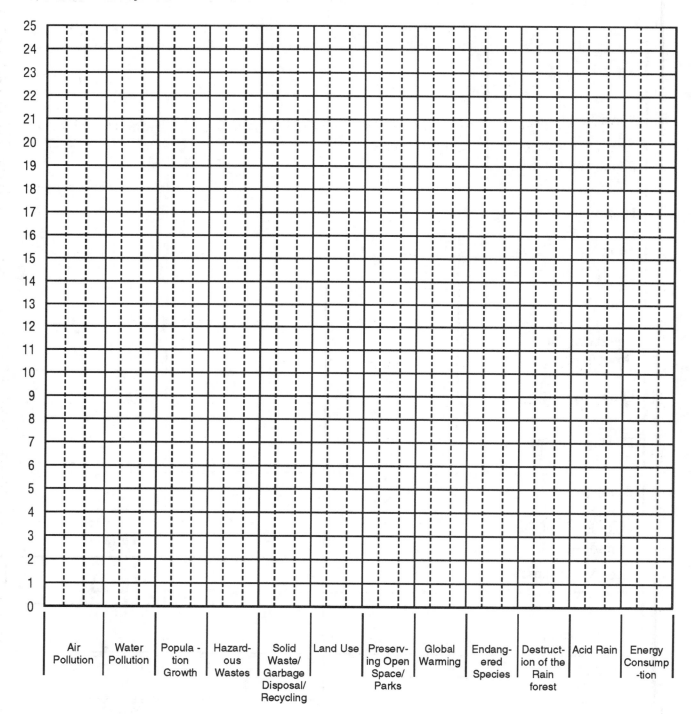

Issues Awareness *(cont.)*

Answer the questions.

1. What category had the most people feeling it was the number one concern?

   _____

2. What category had the fewest people feeling it was a number one problem?

   _____

3. Look over your survey. List five of the reasons people gave for explaining why they chose that issue as number one.

   a. _____

   b. _____

   c. _____

   d. _____

   e. _____

4. What do you feel is the most important issue in ...

   Your Community?_____

   Why? _____

   _____

   Your Country? _____

   Why? _____

   _____

   The World? _____

   Why? _____

Analyzing Environmental Issues

Question

What are the environmental issues and who are the players?

Setting the stage

- Review with students the issues spectrum.

- What was one of the issues?

- What were the different opinions about that issue?

- On what did people base their opinions?

- Discuss with students positions based on facts, on emotion, on belief, on value.

- Have students give examples of each.

Materials Needed for Each Group

- copy of Sample Issue Analysis (page 21), one per student

- copy of Issue Analysis Research Guide (page 22), one per student

- data-capture sheet (page 23), one per student

  Note to the teacher: In this activity the class will be practicing one issue analysis in preparation for continuing analyses to be developed in the students' environmental issues journals. The issues to be analyzed will be presented following the closure section from the majority of lessons in this book. As students become more comfortable with the process of analyzing the issues, you may want to have them work independently. However, to start with, it is best if students work in small groups.

Procedure

1. Review with students the Sample Issue Analysis (page 21) before beginning this activity.
2. Divide class into student groups.
3. Give students an environmental issue to discuss.
4. Have students brainstorm a list of possible positions regarding the issue, a list of players associated with those positions, and a list of values and beliefs that might support those players' positions.
5. Have students assign a spokesperson from their groups to share the group's analysis with the class.
6. Have students place their analyses in their environmental issues journals.

Extensions

Have students create a bulletin board of issues from the newspaper. Hold a debate on an issue that students disagree on. Allow them time to research their positions.

Closure

Have students look over their environmental issues journals at the end of this activity. Have them pick an issue that they feel very strongly about and research that issue in depth. They can use the issues analysis research guide (page 22) to help in their research.

Analyzing Environmental Issues *(cont.)*

Sample Issue Analysis

Issue: Car manufacturers should be forced to develop car models that get no less than 40 mpg (84 kmpg). All other models should be discontinued by the year 2010.

Positions:

Strongly Agree: By forcing companies to design energy efficient cars, we will save natural resources for the future, and we will be less dependent on foreign oil supplies. Besides, if our energy demand gets too large, we will have to extract oil from wilderness areas in Alaska and Canada. This will cause destruction of some of the last remaining wild areas in North America, not to mention the increased risk of transporting oil in barges and pipelines.

Agree: Car manufacturers should be encouraged to design energy efficient cars and be rewarded for good design, but it is unfair to outlaw all other types of cars. That type of efficiency will require smaller cars, but not everyone wants, likes, or fits into smaller cars.

Disagree: Free enterprise is the basis for our economy. If the government places regulations on how and what to design, we will no longer be a free country. Supply and demand rules a democratic economy. The consumer does not care about energy efficiency as much as comfort, style, safety, and longevity. Besides, a more important issue is controlling air pollutants. Smog and exhaust pollution is a much bigger issue than mileage. Why don't we encourage car companies to design cars that run on alternative fuels?

Strongly Disagree: By mandating what kind of cars are made, you eliminate an entire market of cars needed by certain individuals. What if all the cars they design are small and compact? How will the physically disabled be able to use their cars? What about large families? Will the car companies be discriminating against family size? What if a car company cannot come up with an efficient design? Will all the people working for that company lose their jobs? This type of ruling denies freedoms and discriminates.

Players:

- Oil Companies
- Consumers
- Government officials proposing the law
- Luxury car manufacturers
- Foreign car companies

- U.S. car companies

Values and Beliefs:

- Freedom of choice in running a business
- Fear of dependency on foreign oil supplies
- Environmental concerns
- Discriminatory acts
- Freedom of choice in making purchases and having options in economy

- Democratic economy based on supply and demand

Analyzing Environmental Issues *(cont.)*

Issue Analysis Research Guide

Describe the issue you are going to research: _____

What questions do you have about this issue? What would you like to learn more about?

_____

What are the possible sources you could use in your research? (Use primary and secondary resources.)

Questions to explore to help you understand your issue.

1. What is the history of your issue? How long have people disagreed about this issue?

2. How do other countries deal with this issue? Is there more or less disagreement among the citizens?

3. Research specific examples of your players:
    Who is really involved in this issue? _____
    What are their positions about the issue? _____
    What are some statements by the players expressing their opinions?_____

4. What types of laws, regulations, and restrictions exist that could affect your issue?
    Local level? _____
    State level? _____
    National level? _____
    International level?_____

5. What types of nongovernmental organizations are involved in this issue?
    Nonprofit groups? _____
    Lobbying groups? _____
    Corporations? _____
    Small businesses?_____
    What are their positions?_____

6. Interview one or two people who have opinions about this issue. Write your interview questions in advance. Find out what they think. What facts do they use to support their positions? Where do values and beliefs enter into their opinions?

_____

_____

Analyzing Environmental Issues *(cont.)*

Issue Analysis

Positions:

- **Strongly Agree**

  _____
  _____

- **Agree**

  _____
  _____

- **Disagree**

  _____
  _____

- **Strongly Disagree**

  _____
  _____

Values and Beliefs

_____
_____
_____
_____

Players:

_____
_____
_____
_____

Preservationist vs Conservationist

Question

What do environmental leaders mean by *preserve* and *conserve?*

Setting the Stage

- Ask two students to pre-read these two roles. Then, ask them to read them aloud after you describe an issue.

Issue Description To Be Read by Teacher

In the western United States there is a mountain range that has been undeveloped and protected. It has huge forests with some of the largest trees in the state. It has two rivers that start in the mountains themselves. To the west of the range is a large national park; to the east is a growing community; to the north and west are small towns.

Role One

I have lived in these mountains all my life. I grew up hiking on that mountain, and you will never see trees, plants, and animals like there are on that mountain. Some of the biggest trees I've ever seen grow on that mountain. I regularly see wildlife like owls, moose, wolves, mountain goats, and eagles that I do not see in other mountains. I drink out of both streams that run down that mountain. I'd like to save that mountain forever and make it a wilderness area so that the plants, animals, and land will be protected for many generations to come. Our children deserve to experience this pristine wilderness.

Role Two

I too have lived in these mountains all my life. I've grown up hiking in the mountains and have seen the same trees and wildlife. It is a spectacular place and one that many people should be allowed to enjoy. However, I've also lived in this area long enough to know that there aren't a whole lot of ways to make money...that mountain is money. First of all, there is great timber potential. We could be harvesting some of those trees for lumber that our country so desperately needs. Actually, those trees need to be harvested pretty soon or they will just die, and what good is a dead tree! People in this community need jobs, and a timber industry could provide jobs. We can use the resources of the mountain wisely but at the same time enjoy all its beauty. There is no reason hikers and campers can't get along with a timber company. Besides, we can provide a lot of new habitat for the animals of that mountain; clearing out a big space would create all kinds of new plants for animals to eat. We can use our resources wisely and still enjoy the mountain for generations to come.

- Outline the major points of the two roles. What is each person advocating?

Preservationist vs Conservationist *(cont.)*

Materials Needed for Each Individual
- copy of Preservationist/Conservationist Outline (page 27)
- copy of addresses of National Environmental Organizations (pages 28-29)
- envelopes
- stamps
- writing paper

Procedure

1. Introduce to students the terms *preserve* and *conserve* and the terms *preservationists* and *conservationists.* (Preservationists advocate preserving the land and the resources. Conservationists advocate a wise use of the resources and multiple uses of land.)

2. Have students identify from the roles read which was preservationist and which was conservationist. Ask what were the key phrases and terms that helped them to identify the position of each player?

3. Discuss with the class their opinions about whether someone can be a preservationist and conservationist at the same time. What are the factors and values that help a person to decide on a position?

4. In this activity, students will write the different organizations, requesting information about their goals, projects, etc. Each student should write a different organization. See pages 28-29 for a list of addresses.

5. It might also be helpful for students to request the organization's position on a current environmental issue.

6. Discuss with students the difference between *persuasion* and *propaganda.* How might organizations or individuals use these skills to convince others of their position.

7. Once students have received the information back from the organizations, they should use the Preservationist/Conservationist Outline (page 27) to help them analyze the literature.

8. Have students share the information they gained from the different organizations. Have them post the flyers, stickers, booklets, pamphlets, etc., that they received.

9. Discuss with students the role of environmental organizations in politics (lobbying, awareness, education, fund raising, etc.). What other organizations are involved in environmental issues? (governmental, local groups, concerned political groups, religious groups, etc.)

Preservationist vs Conservationist *(cont.)*

Extensions

- Invite local branch representatives to speak to your class about their organization.
- Have students survey newspaper articles for positions on environmental issues. Are the positions conservation or preservation?
- Have students survey community members for their support of environmental organizations. Which groups do they support? Why do they support them?

Closure

- Have students write a role play for the Alaskan wilderness issue from the position of a conservationist and then a preservationist.
- Have students write a persuasive statement that would clearly demonstrate a conservation position or a preservation position.
- Have students share the role plays.
- In their environmental issues journals, have students pick an organization that best supports their feelings and tell why they support them. What issues do they deal with that are important? What information has particularly influenced them?

Issue Analysis: Alaskan Wilderness

Alaska has a great deal of oil as a natural resource. It is also one of the largest wilderness areas left in the United States. Our country is very dependent on foreign oil for our industries, cars, and energy for our homes. Some people feel we should start drilling for more oil in Alaska to support our energy needs. Others feel we should protect the Alaskan wilderness.

Preservationist vs
Conservationist *(cont.)*

Preservationist/Conservationist Outline

Answer the following questions in preparation for a class discussion. It is important that you read all the information your organization sends you.

Name of organization you wrote: _____

1. Describe the types of information they sent you—letters, pamphlets, stickers, bumper stickers, solicitations for funding, etc.

   _____

   _____

   _____

2. After reading their literature, what do you see as their primary goal as an organization?

   _____

   _____

   _____

3. Pick one or two sentences from their literature that you feel best sum up this organization's mission or goal.

   _____

   _____

   _____

4. What do you think would attract people to support this group?

   _____

   _____

   _____

5. What do think would make people not support this group?

   _____

   _____

   _____

6. Would you be willing to support this group? Why or why not?

   _____

   _____

   _____

Preservationist vs Conservationist *(cont.)*

Organizations and Agencies

American Conservation Association 30 Rockefeller Plaza New York, New York 10112	Greenpeace USA 1436 U Street, NW Washington, DC 20009
Animal Welfare Institute P.O. Box 3650 Washington, DC 20007	Center for Marine Conservation 1725 DeSales Street, NW, #500 Washington, DC 20036
Chesapeake Bay Foundation 162 Prince George Street Annapolis, MD 21401	Defenders of Wildlife 1244 19th Street, NW Washington, DC 20036
Earth Island Institute 300 Broadway, Suite 28 San Francisco, CA 94133	Friends of the Earth 218 D Street, SE Washington, DC 20003
American Forestry Association 1510 P Street, NW Washington, DC 20036	National Audubon Society 950 Third Avenue New York, NY 10022
National Parks Service Department of the Interior Office of Public Affairs P.O. Box 37127 Washington, DC 20013	Environmental Defense Fund 257 Park Avenue South New York, NY 10010

Preservationist vs Conservationist *(cont.)*

Organizations and Agencies

National Resources Council of America 1015 31st Street, NW Washington, DC 20007	National Resources Defense Council 90 New Montgomery Street, Ste. 620 San Francisco, CA 94105
National Wildlife Federation 8925 Leesburg Pike Vienna, VA 22184-0001	The Nature Conservancy 1815 North Lynn Street Arlington, VA 22209
The Sierra Club Public Affairs Department San Francisco, CA 94109	Soil and Water Conservation Society 7515 Northeast Ankeny Road Ankeny, IA 50021
Student Conservation Association P.O. Box 550C Charlestown, NH 03603	U.S. Environmental Protection Agency 401 M Street, SW Washington, DC 20460
The Wilderness Society 1400 I Street, NW Washington, DC 20005	Worldwatch Institute 1776 Massachusetts Ave., NW Washington, DC 20036
World Wildlife Fund 1250 24th Street, NW Washington, DC 20037	National Arbor Day Foundation 100 Arbor Avenue Nebraska City, NE 68410

Just the Facts

Garbage, trash, junk—it is all the same. We throw it out. Paper, plastic, metal, glass—it is all garbage. It is all solid waste.

Nature does not make any trash, garbage, or solid waste. Everything in nature is used to feed another animal or help a plant grow. There is no waste in nature's cycle. But in the human cycle, there is much waste. In fact, the average individual throws away three and one-half to four and one-half pounds of trash a day. How much trash is that in a year?

Each year our population grows, and with it our solid waste amounts grow. Where does the trash go? How can we make less trash?

Key Words

Landfill—A place where solid waste is deposited. It is a modern-day dump that protects the groundwater. Our trash is buried in a huge hole and then covered over. We do not have enough landfills for all the solid waste we produce.

Recycle—Many of the items we throw away are *non-biodegradable*, which means they will never decompose or rot. They will stay in the landfill for hundreds of years. We can reduce the amount of solid waste that goes into a landfill by recycling. Different states have different laws about recycling, but currently the technology exists to recycle cardboard, newspaper, white paper, glass, aluminum, metal cans, and many types of plastics.

Reuse—We can also reduce the amount of solid waste by reusing things we would usually throw away. For example, we can reuse the bags from the grocery store. We can wash plastic cups and silverware after a picnic. We can donate toys we do not want anymore and clothes we have outgrown to children who can use them.

Compost—We can also reduce the amount of solid waste by composting. Instead of putting leaves, sticks, grass clippings, vegetable, and fruit scraps in the trash, we can compost them. Set up a place for these things to decompose, and you will be reducing the amount of solid waste going to a landfill. These materials are called *biodegradable.* These rotten materials will eventually become fertilizer for plants and gardens. At the same time, we are reducing solid waste that goes to the landfill.

Incinerator—In some places, solid waste is not sent to the landfill; it is sent to an incinerator. An incinerator burns the trash and then sends the ash to a landfill. To protect the air, there are many regulations on the burning of solid waste.

Reduce, Reuse, Recycle

Question

What is the trash problem?

Setting the Stage

- Prior to class, collect four pounds of trash. Be sure it is a mixture of trash with some pieces which can be reused and recycled.

- Ask your class to sit down in a circle, and then pour the entire bag of trash in the middle of the circle. Announce to your class this represents the average amount of trash a person produces per day in the United States. Estimate the weight of the trash and then weigh it. Calculate the amounts per week, month, and year. Where does all this trash go?

- Ask each student to draw a series of pictures describing where the trash goes. Have them explain the pictures once completed.

Materials Needed for Entire Class

- 4-5 lbs (1.8-2.5 kg) of trash
- drawing paper
- colored markers or crayons
- selection of books, magazines, and articles on solid waste
- large glass/clear plastic jar
- rich soil (Avoid potting soil. The soil must have organisms and bacteria that can help in decomposition.)
- copy of Treasure Hunt Word List (page 33), one per student

    Note to the teacher: Your students are going to go on an information treasure hunt.

Procedure

1. Split your class into small groups. Each group will have the week to research the list of words on page 33. They will receive points for each word. The group with the most points wins the treasure hunt.

2. Points are assigned as follows:

    1 point: for a written definition of the word.

    3 points: for a picture that demonstrates or explains the word.

    5 points: for a demonstration, model, or actual object that explains the meaning of the word.

3. Groups may not share information with other groups. All groups must meet the deadline.

4. Each group should be given a checklist to keep track of their progress. On the deadline, everyone in the group must participate in explaining their progress.

5. Based on the students' research, post a list of recyclable materials in the classroom.

Reduce, Reuse, Recycle *(cont.)*

Extensions

- Invite a representative from your community's solid waste management office to speak to your class about solid waste, recycling, and reducing.
- Visit a landfill or a trash-to-steam plant in your area.
- Have students interview a local garbage collector.
- Have students watch one of the many videos on solid waste. (See bibliography for sample titles.)

Closure

Have students make a model landfill. Fill a large glass/clear plastic container with layers of dirt and pieces of trash. Sprinkle a small amount of water on it. Have them make predictions as to what will happen, and record these in their environmental issues journals. Then, have them make regular observations and record any changes that occur.

Issue Analysis: Landfill space and cost.

By the year 2009, eighty percent of landfills that exist today will be full. A new landfill can cost up to $90 million.

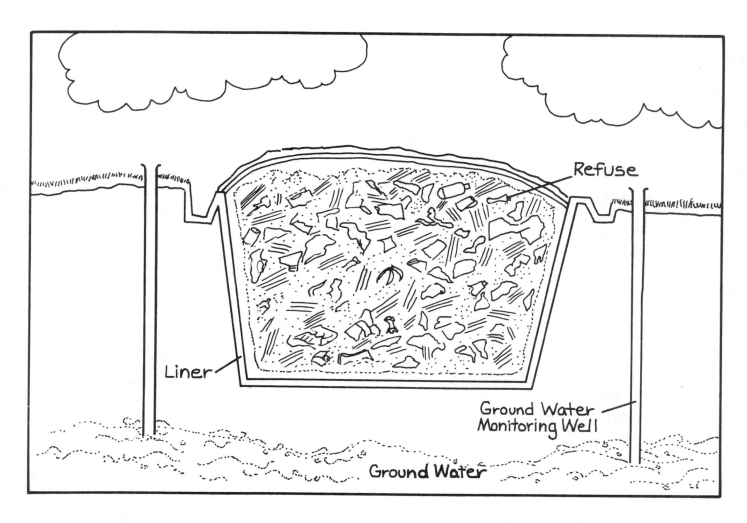

Reduce, Reuse, Recycle *(cont.)*

Treasure Hunt Word List

Research as many of these as possible in the coming days. Definitions earn one point.
Pictures earn three points. Demonstrations, models, or objects earn five points.

1. Solid waste ....
2. Recycle ....
3. Reusable solid waste ....
4. Household hazardous waste ....
5. Landfill ....
6. Solid waste incinerator ....
7. Decomposition ....
8. Ground water contamination ....
9. Composting ....
10. Disposable products ....
11. Solid waste management ....
12. NIMBY (Not in My Back Yard) ....
13. Yard waste ....
14. Heavy metals ....
15. High grade paper ....
16. Organic waste ....
17. Inorganic waste ....
18. Renewable resource ....
19. Non-renewable resource ....
20. Combustion and ash ....
21. Municipal Solid Waste (MSW) ....
22. Biodegradable ....
23. Non-biodegradable ....

My Trash, Your Trash

Question

What can I do to help solve the trash problem?

Setting the Stage

- Give each student a paper grocery bag and a small plastic bag.
- Ask them to decorate the bags since they are going to be very important for them over the next 24 hours.
- Assign students to carry the bags with them for the next 24 hours. Everything they would usually throw away should go into the bag. Things thrown out in meal preparation should also go into the bag. Scraps and food pieces should be put into the plastic bag.
- Ask each student to predict how much trash they will produce in 24 hours.

Materials Needed for Each Group

- scales
- large graph to record trash collection results
- markers
- calculators
- data-capture sheet (page 35), one per student

Procedure

1. Have each student weigh his/her trash and then record the amount on a class graph.
2. Then ask each student to put his/her trash into the following groups: reuse, recycle, compost, and trash to be thrown out. Then have them count the number of pieces in each group and calculate the percentages on their data-capture sheets.
3. Have students compare the results of their calculations.

Extensions

- Have students find out about the recycling opportunities in their communities.
- Have students find out if their communities have any opportunities for composting, especially leaves, branches, and Christmas trees.
- Set up a compost bin in your classroom for snack and lunch waste.

Closure

In their environmental issues journals, have students summarize the ways they can reduce the amount of trash they produce in a week. They should list 5-10 ways.

Issue Analysis: NIMBY (Not In My Back Yard)

Of people surveyed in a 1990 National Solid Waste Management Association survey, 50–60% said they would not want a new landfill in their backyard.

My Trash, Your Trash *(cont.)*

Fill in the information needed.

Part I.

Weigh your trash. Total weight of trash and bags _____

Sort your trash into four piles: recycle, reuse, compost, and trash to be thrown out. Then count the pieces in each pile and record on the chart below.

Number of pieces that can be recycled_____

Number of pieces that can be reused_____

Number of pieces that could be composted _____

Number of pieces that must be thrown out_____

Total Number of Pieces of Trash _____

Part II.

Calculate the percentages of your trash.

1. **Percentage Recyclable**

   Total pieces of recycled trash ÷ Total pieces of trash = _____ x 100 = _____

   _____ ÷ _____ = _____ x 100 = _____ % of recycled trash

2. **Percentage Reusable**

   Total pieces reusable ÷ Total pieces of trash = _____ x 100 = _____

   _____ ÷ _____ = _____ x 100 = _____ % of reusable trash

3. **Percentage Compost**

   Total pieces of compost ÷ Total pieces of trash = _____ x 100 = _____

   _____ ÷ _____ = _____ x 100 = _____ % of compost trash

4. **Percentage to throw out**

   Total number thrown out ÷Total number of pieces of trash = x 100 = _____

   _____ ÷ _____ = _____ x 100 = _____ % to be thrown out

Packaging and Precycling

Question

How are packaging and solid waste management related?

Setting the Stage

- Have students brainstorm a list of daily activities that occur in their home. For example: showering, washing clothes, cooking dinner, etc.
- Next to each activity ask students to list some consumer products that might be used. For example: showering—soap, shampoo.
- After each product, have students list the type of packaging material that is primarily used (plastic, glass, metal, paper, other, none).
- Once the activity is completed, have students tally up the totals on the packaging. What type of packaging is most common? Is it biodegradable? Is it recyclable? How do you know?

Materials Needed for Entire Class

- a selection of products from the grocery store (with clearly marked prices, all from the same basic item—for example, POTATO: french fries, canned potatoes, potato chips, potato buds, whole potatoes.) Other suggestions include tomatoes and apples.
- calculators
- copy of Product Analysis sheet (page 38), one per student (Record the names of products on the Product Analysis sheet before giving to students.)

Procedure

1. Have students brainstorm a list of products in a grocery store developed from either a potato, a tomato, or an apple.
2. Have students look over the list and predict which items would be the most expensive and which would be the least expensive. What are the reasons for the differences in price, even though they are all from the same ingredient?
3. Give each pair of students one of the products. They are to record the weight, the price, the price-per-ounce (gram), and the primary packaging. You may need to review how many ounces (grams) are in a pound (kilogram).
4. Go through the list and ask each pair of students to share their results. Everyone should fill in the price-per-ounce (gram).
5. Have students review their list and their predictions. Which cost the most? Which cost the least?
6. Ask students if there is any relationship between the type of packaging and the cost. What is that relationship?
7. Ask students what the serving sizes are for the different products. Is there a relationship between the type of packaging and the number of servings present in that package?
8. Ask students why companies package products in different materials.

Extensions

- Have students visit a grocery store and take a survey of primary packaging materials.
- Have students research the history of different packaging materials: plastic, aluminum, steel, and glass. Where do these products come from? How are they processed? What are the expenses associated with their production?

Packaging and Precycling *(cont.)*

Closure

- Have students think about the original lesson where they dumped four pounds of trash on the floor. Our goal through these lessons on solid waste has been to reduce the amount of solid waste. The term used for reducing the amount of solid waste before it enters our home is *precycling*.

- Ask students how they would precycle while shopping? Have them brainstorm a list of products. Then, for homework ask everyone to look through their kitchen cupboards and find the product that they think deserves the award for the best environmental packaging. Also, have them find the product that deserves the award for the worst environmental packaging. Have students bring the products into school and explain why they were chosen. Make a display of the products. Discuss with students alternatives for the worst packaging award items.

Issue Analysis: Consumerism and Solid Waste Management

85% of American babies wear "disposable" diapers. That adds up to close to 16 million diapers a year. Estimation of the time it takes for decomposition of "degradable" diapers is 500 years in a modern landfill. How does a parent choose between cloth and "disposable" diapers? (Taken from the 1992 Environmental Almanac by World Resources Institute.)

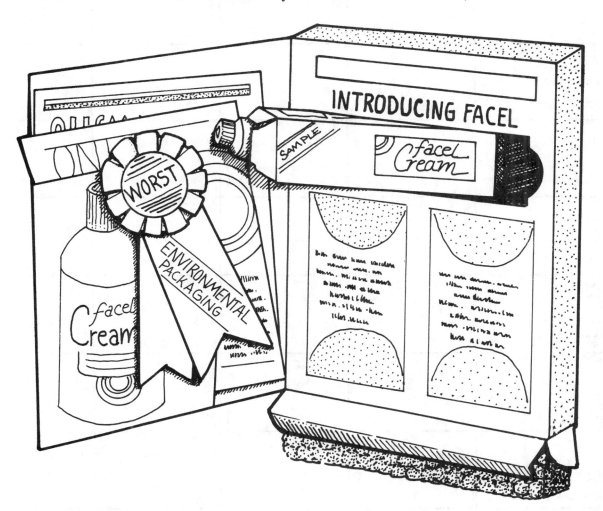

Packaging and Precycling *(cont.)*

Product Analysis

Record the weight, price, and price-per-ounce (gram) of your product. Pick the primary packaging material from this list and record it on the chart. Primary Packaging Options: plastic, glass, metal, paper (cardboard), other, none.

Product	Weight	Price	Price/Ounce or Gram	Primary Packaging
1.				
2.				
3.				
4.				
5.				
6.				
7.				
8.				

Household Hazardous Wastes

Question

What types of hazardous products are in my home?

Setting the Stage

- Bring into class a selection of the following products: air freshener, drain opener, floor finish, polish, toilet bowl cleaner, oven cleaner, glue, paint, paint thinner, varnish, antifreeze, battery, fertilizer, herbicides, pesticides, pet treatment for fleas and ticks.

- Brainstorm with your class the things all these products have in common.

- Bring up the fact that all of them can be very hazardous. They may be toxic, corrosive, flammable, and even explosive. Examine the containers and see how many list the ingredients and how many have a DANGER or POISON label on them.

- Tell students it is important to note that these products are toxic in different concentrations. Some have such low levels of toxins that they are not a threat. However, if some are ingested, inhaled, or absorbed, they can potentially damage the nervous system, kidneys, liver, and reproductive system.

- Ask students why we should be concerned about throwing out these empty containers. Review with your class how trash is disposed. There is a fear that toxic materials thrown out with the trash may pollute drinking water and degrade air quality (especially if they are taken to an incinerator).

Materials Needed for Each Group

- lemon juice
- borax
- vinegar
- abrasive cleaner
- furniture polish
- paper towels
- cloth rags
- dirty pots/pans
- olive/vegetable oil
- lemons
- water
- ammonia-based window cleaner
- spray bottles
- newspapers
- sponges
- windows, mirrors, wood furniture
- copy of Household Hazardous Materials Audit (page 42), one per student
- data-capture sheet (page 43), three copies per student

Household Hazardous Wastes *(cont.)*

Procedure

1. Assign each student to do a Household Hazardous Materials Audit. Review with your class the procedure to follow. They should check the items they find in their homes and record the storage places. Share the home audits. What materials were most common? Where were the majority of the products stored? Why is storage an important issue? How many of the products had WARNING or POISON labels? Discuss with your class the concept of degrees of toxicity. Some products are very toxic (oil based paints and paint strippers) while others are not very toxic, like detergents.

2. Brainstorm with your class reasons to reduce household hazardous wastes. (Contamination of ground water and air; landfills filling up, etc.)

3. Brainstorm with your class ways to reduce household wastes.

4. Introduce to students the concept of Alternative Products.

   In this final section, your students will be doing product comparison of three types of products: furniture polish, window cleaner, and abrasive cleaner. Each group of students will test the toxic product versus the non-toxic product and compare the results. Have students complete their data-capture sheets prior to the discussion of this activity. Students should use one data-capture sheet for each comparison made.

5. Comparison Preparation:

   - **Area to be cleaned:** *counter tops, sinks, dirty pots and pans. Use sponge to apply and scrub.*

     Home product to be tested: abrasive cleaner—eg., Comet, Ajax.

     Alternative product to be tested: You will be dipping a half of lemon into borax.

   - **Area to be cleaned:** *windows or mirrors.*

     Home Product to be tested: ammonia-based window cleaner. Use paper towels to clean.

     Alternative product to be tested: 1/2 cup (118 mL) of vinegar mixed with 8 cups (2.72 L) of water. Use pieces of newspaper to clean.

   - **Area to be cleaned:** *wood furnishings.*

     Home product to be tested: furniture polish. Use cloth rag to clean with.

     Alternative product to be tested: 1/4 cup (59 mL) of lemon juice mixed with 1/2 cup (118 mL) of olive or vegetable oil. Use cloth rag to clean.

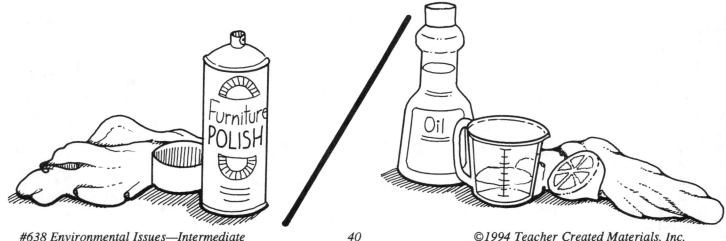

Household Hazardous Wastes *(cont.)*

Extensions

- Invite the local Poison Control Center to speak to your class about dealing with poisons in the home: storage, emergency responses, etc.
- Invite an organic gardener to speak to your class about alternative products used for weed and pest control in the garden, along with alternatives to fertilizers.
- Have students research their community's plan for hazardous waste disposal. Are there oil recycling containers at service stations?
- Do you have a hazardous waste trash pick-up day? If not, find out why. (The reason is usually cost.)
- Have students find out what laws there are about hazardous wastes in their state.
- Have students find out where hazardous wastes are disposed/stored.
- Have students write to the Citizens' Clearinghouse for Hazardous Waste, PO Box 926, Arlington, VA 22216, for information about hazardous wastes and other product alternatives.

Closure

- Discuss with students the advantages and disadvantages of the home and alternative products.
- Discuss with students why consumers buy different products.
- Have students brainstorm ways to educate people about alternative products.
- In their environmental issues journals, have students write letters to the editor of the local paper, advocating the need for hazardous waste disposal in your community. Include suggestions for ways to reduce the amount of hazardous waste produced. Then, have them make copies and mail their letters.

Issue Analysis: Amount of Household Hazardous Waste Produced

The amount of household hazardous wastes that enter the water system by way of household drains or unchecked into landfills is estimated at 300,000 tons per year. (*1992 Environmental Almanac*, World Resource Institute). What can be done to control the numbers of toxins entering our water and waste stream? Can we challenge industry to produce products that contain fewer or no toxins? Would consumers be willing to pay more for a nontoxic cleaner?

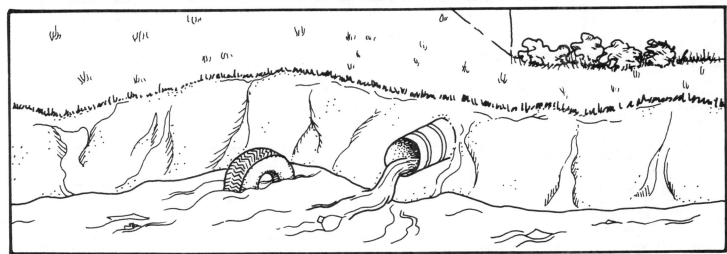

Household Hazardous Wastes *(cont.)*

Household Hazardous Materials Audit

Go through your cabinets and closets and check off the items you have in your home. Describe where each is stored. Check if it has a poison label or danger warning.

Checklist	Storage	Poison/Danger Warning
Laundry:		
spot remover		
starch spray		
bleach powder		
bleach liquid		
moth balls		
Cleaning		
carpet and upholstery		
furniture polish		
scouring powder		
oven cleaner		
ammonia		
floor cleaner		
toilet bowl cleaner		
disinfectant		
drain opener		
glass cleaner		
Other:		
herbicides		
insecticides		
insect repellent		
no-pest strips		
hair coloring		
home hair permanent		
nail polish		
nail polish remover		
flea collar, shampoo		
used motor oil		
antifreeze		
air freshener		
paint thinner		
oil-based paint		
varnish		
paint stripper; finish remover		
typewriter correction fluid		
old batteries		
ant/roach killer		
rat/mouse poison		
permanent ink markers		

Household Hazardous Wastes *(cont.)*

You and your group will be comparing the effectiveness of two types of household products: toxic and nontoxic. You will need to record your observations very carefully.

Read through the entire analysis before you begin.

1. Describe the item to be cleaned.

   _____

   _____

2. Clean one-half with the home product and the other half with the alternative product.

   _____

   _____

3. Compare the results. Check off which applies:

   The home product side is cleaner._____

   The alternative product side is cleaner. _____

   Both sides are equally clean._____

4. Describe the advantages and disadvantages of each product.

   Home product: _____

      Advantages:_____

      Disadvantages: _____

   Alternative product: _____

      Advantages:_____

      Disadvantages: _____

5. If you were to use one of the two products, which would you choose? Explain your reason for picking that product.

   _____

   _____

Just the Facts

For many years people have been adding things into the air that we breathe. We add small particles anytime we burn something, even if we are using wood to heat our homes. Think of all the ways just today you added something to the air. Did you ride in a car or bus? Did you use a spray bottle? Did you use electricity? Did you turn on a heater or air conditioner? All of these activities have added something to the air that you breathe. Some of these pollutants are not very harmful, some are harmful, and some, scientists are unsure of. We do know that when we burn fossil fuels (oil, coal, natural gas, and gasoline), we cause problems in the air. Keep in mind that the air you breathe enters your body through your mouth and nose. If there is pollution in the air, more than likely it can and will get into your body.

Key Words

Particulates—small particles from substances that have been burned. Included are ash, smoke, soot, and dust.

pH—a scale used to measure whether things are acids, bases, or neutral.

Acid—a solution with a pH from 0 – 6.9. Strong acids are lower numbers: 1, 2, and 3; weaker acids are higher numbers: 4, 5, and 6.

Base—solution with a pH from 7.1 – 14. A weak base is 8, 9, and 10 and a strong base is 11, 12, 13, and 14.

Neutral—a solution with a pH of 7.0.

Litmus Paper—an indicator paper used to test if something is acid or base.

Hydrion Paper—an indicator paper used to test the pH of a solution. The paper will give a rough estimate on the pH scale from 0 – 14.

Acid Rain—rain which is made more acidic than usual. When fossil fuels are burned, they produce sulfur dioxide. When this compound is added to precipitation, the pH is changed to a stronger acid (normal rain/snowfall is slightly acidic). Acid rain can kill fish and plants in lakes without soils and rocks which can buffer the acid. Buffering is balancing an acid with a base.

Greenhouse Effect—the natural process of holding in the right amount of heat from the sun so that life can survive on earth. It is an important process because without it, the earth would be too cold to live on.

Global Warming Theory—the theory that because of increased greenhouse gases (CO_2, methane, and nitrous oxides) more heat is being trapped around the earth than should be. The theory is that the earth could warm up to such a point that our climate could change.

What's That in the Air?

Question

How can we see air pollutants?

Setting the Stage

Survey your class on these three questions:

What is air pollution? Where does it come from? What are some effects of air pollution?

Materials Needed for Each Individual

- index cards
- string
- hand lenses or microscopes
- transparent tape
- scissors
- data-capture sheet (page 46)

Note to the teacher: Students will be collecting evidence of air pollution (mostly particulate matter and dust) through the use of an air pollution card.

Procedure

1. Each student will make 3 air pollution cards.
2. Tell students to cut a hole about the size of a silver dollar in the center of each card. The hole is then covered over with transparent tape. The sticky side of the tape is exposed. A string is then attached to the card so that the card can be hung.
3. Have students write *Please Do Not Touch* on the card so passersby will not disturb the test.
4. Brainstorm a list of places where students think there might be air pollutants. Ask students to explain why they think there might be pollutants in that area.
5. Have students hang the cards in the agreed upon locations.
6. Each time the cards are checked, students should use hand lenses or microscopes to identify specific shapes and quantities of particulates on the card.
7. After each card has been tested for the appropriate amount of time, have students glue the cards on their data-capture sheets in the appropriate place and post in the classroom after one week.

Extensions

- Have students research the Clean Air Act. What is it? What is the goal? When was it started?
- Have students compare the United States to other countries in their air quality and the regulations for controlling air quality.

Closure

- Have students survey their cards. Which cards had the greatest amount of particulate matter? Which had the least?
- Discuss with students the reasons behind the varying amounts at different locations.
- Have students make a list of possible sources of particulates in the testing areas. Then, in their environmental issues journals, have students make a list of possible ways to reduce particulate types of pollution.

Issue Analysis: Wood as a Source of Heat.

In many mountain towns and cities, people use firewood to heat their homes. Because of particulates in the air from all the burning, cities are starting to ban fires on certain days.

What's That in the Air? *(cont.)*

Glue each card under the appropriate time period.

24 Hours
3 Days
1 Week

pH Balanced Shampoo...
pH Balanced Air

Question

What is pH and how does it relate to air pollution?

Setting the Stage

- Survey your class for ways they have heard the term pH used. Some students may recall testing the pH in their pool, testing the pH in an aquarium, pH balanced shampoo and deodorant advertisements.

- Survey your class on the terms *acid, base*, and *alkaline*. Find out what they know and what their misconceptions are about these terms.

Materials Needed for Entire Class

- litmus paper
- Hydrion paper
- selection of acid, base, and neutral liquids (e.g. acids: lemon juice, vinegar, tomato juice, tap water; bases: milk of magnesia, lime water, tap water; and neutral: distilled water)
- copy of incomplete pH scale (page 49), one per student
- paper cups or dip cups for sauces, ketchup, etc.
- plastic gloves
- safety glasses
- copy of Acid Rain Research Guide (page 50), one per student
- data-capture sheet (page 51), one per student

Procedure

1. Introduce to students the pH scale. Draw a scale on the chalkboard and give each student a copy of the pH scale (page 49). Have students repeat your steps on their charts. Write in the numbers on the scale: 0 – 14. Write in the words *neutral: 7, acid: 4–6.9, very acidic: 0–3, base: 7.1–10, very basic (alkaline): 10 – 14.*

2. Explain to students that acids and bases can burn if you are not careful, so everyone will be wearing safety glasses and gloves. (If you do not have access to these materials, be careful to use diluted liquids.) In case any liquid splashes in a student's eye, rinse thoroughly immediately. STRESS SAFETY.

3. There are two ways for your students to measure pH. First, litmus paper tells if a substance is an acid, base, or neutral. Demonstrate the use of the paper. Pink paper turns blue for bases; blue paper turns pink for acid. Give each student a selection of liquids to test. Have them record their results on their data-capture sheets. The second way to measure pH is using Hydrion paper. By dipping this paper in a liquid and matching the paper to the color chart on the tube, students can tell the exact pH level.

4. Ask students to return to their test cups. Ask them to predict the pH level for each liquid. Remind them that the litmus test already told them whether it is an acid or base. Once they have made their predictions, students should test the liquids and record their results on their data-capture sheets.

5. Then have students write in the liquids on their pH scales.

6. For additional activities, students can bring in samples of liquids from home to be tested.

pH Balanced Shampoo...
pH Balanced Air? *(cont.)*

Extensions

- Invite a chemist to speak to your class about acids and bases.
- Have students test products that advertise to be pH balanced and see if they really are.

Closure

- Discuss with your class the practice of burning fossil fuels. Why must we burn coal and oil? Where do we burn them? When fossil fuels are burned, they produce two by-products which are then emitted into the air: sulfur dioxide and nitrogen oxides. When these two substances combine with atmospheric water, acid rain is formed.
- Have students collect rain water in their area. Test the pH and then record the results in the environmental issues journals, as well as brainstorm possible dangers of acid rain. Examples: harmful to plants, harmful to animals that live in water, breaks down stone and rocks in statues and buildings.

Issue Analysis: Long Range Transport of Acids

- Canada has an acid rain problem because of manufacturing in the mid-western states of the United States. The sulfur dioxides are produced in the industries in Ohio, Illinois, and Pennsylvania and are carried over the land by the weather patterns. The acids then combine with rain over Canada and the Adirondack mountains in New York, making many of those lakes lifeless due to acid rain.
- Using the Acid Rain Research Guide (page 50), research areas in the world that have been particularly affected by acid rain.
- Places to research include the Adirondacks, Eastern Canada, Poland, Sweden, Germany, Midwestern United States, England. Share the answers to the research.

48

pH Balanced Shampoo...pH Balanced Air *(cont.)*

pH Scale

Fill in the numbers 0 – 14 on this line as your teacher explains the pH scale. Write in these words once your teacher has explained the pH strengths and weaknesses: Neutral, Acid, Strong Acid, Base, and Strong Base.

Safety:

Strong acids and strong bases can burn you. Be very careful handling these solutions. If you spill any, notify your teacher at once and rinse off whatever you spilled!

pH Balanced Shampoo...
pH Balanced Air *(cont.)*

Acid Rain Research Guide

Use the questions to help guide your research for a country or location in the world that has been affected by acid rain.

Country or Location to Research

1. What type of air pollution is found in this country?

   _____

   _____

2. How has acid rain affected this place? Give examples.

   _____

   _____

3. What is being done to clean the air?

   _____

   _____

4. Some countries may not produce the acids, but the acids may travel in the weather patterns from other countries and be dumped hundreds of miles away from the source. This is called *Long Range Transport*. Is your location impacted by the sulfur dioxide and nitrogen oxides from other places? If so, from where are these chemicals coming?

   _____

   _____

   _____

   _____

pH Balanced Shampoo...
pH Balanced Air *(cont.)*

Step One: Test each solution using the litmus paper. Write in whether it is an acid, base, or neutral.

Step Two: Predict an actual pH number for the solution. Remember to refer to your pH scale.

Step Three: Test each solution using the Hydrion paper. Record the number you get when you match the color of the paper with the color chart on the Hydrion paper container.

Solution	Litmus Test	Prediction	Hydrion Paper Result
1.			
2.			
3.			
4.			
5.			
6.			
7.			

Warming Right Up

Question

What is the greenhouse effect?

Setting the Stage

- Survey your class for their understanding of global warming.
- Have students make a list entitled What We Know about Global Warming. Post the list in your classroom so that it can be referred to throughout the next two lessons. Whenever one of the items on the list is supported or refuted, point it out to your class.

Materials Needed for Each Group

- 2 clear two-liter soda bottles
- 2 thermometers
- 2 cups (500 g) of potting soil
- clip-on lamps, shop lamps, any kind of steady light source
- plastic wrap
- rubber band
- tape
- data-capture sheets (pages 54-55), one each per student

Note to the teacher: Tell students the following: Each group will build a mini greenhouse. Follow the directions carefully. Record the temperature on your data-capture sheet (page 54). (Read through all the directions before starting.)

Procedure *(Student Instructions)*

1. Cut off the tops of the soda bottles. Both bottles must be exactly the same size. Remove the labels from the bottles. If the labels will not come off, fill bottles with hot water. The hot water will loosen the glue so you can pull off the labels.

2. Pour 1 cup (250 g) of potting soil into the base of the soda bottle.

3. Tape a thermometer into the inside of the bottle. The entire thermometer must be on the inside of the soda bottle. Tape the thermometer so the numbers are facing out; you must be able to read the numbers on the thermometer.

4. Put a piece of plastic wrap over the top of one of the soda bottles and seal it shut with a rubber band. Leave the other soda bottle open.

5. Record the temperature of both soda bottles on your data-capture sheet. Write your predictions as to what you think will happen to each soda bottle over the ten-minute time period.

6. Place both soda bottles under the light source. Be sure that each is the same distance from the light and is getting the same amount of heat and light energy from the lamp.

7. Continue to record the temperature of both bottles every thirty seconds for the next 10 minutes. Be sure to record the exact temperature.

8. After the first 10 minutes, you may stop recording but in 20 more minutes, a total of 30 minutes from the starting time and again at the 60 minute mark, record the temperature of both soda bottles.

9. When you are finished with this experience, be sure to answer the questions on your data-capture sheet (page 55).

Warming Right Up (*cont.*)

Extensions

- Have students visit a greenhouse and record the temperatures that occur during the day.
- Have students conduct the same test outdoors in the sunlight. How do the results compare?
- Invite an architect to your class to explain passive solar energy and the ways windows and location can play a critical role in heating a home.
- Have students research ozone depletion.

Closure

- Explain to your students that the model greenhouses they made are just like the earth. The soda bottle stands for the earth. The soil stands for the ground. The plastic wrap represents the atmosphere surrounding the earth. The earth is kept warm by a layer of our atmosphere. We would not survive on this planet if it were not for the greenhouse effect. The layer contains greenhouse gases (carbon dioxide, methane, nitrous oxide) that absorb just the right amount of heat so that plants and animals can survive on the earth. The rest of the heat is reflected back out of the atmosphere.
- Explain to students that many people confuse greenhouse effect and global warming. The greenhouse effect is a good thing, for it allows us to live on this planet. The global warming theory states that certain gases, mainly increasing amounts of carbon dioxide due to fossil fuels being burned, are trapping more heat and preventing the heat of the earth from escaping. This trapping of the heat in the greenhouse gases, according to the global warming theory, is causing the average temperature of the planet to increase.
- In their environmental issues journals, have students summarize the meaning of the greenhouse effect and its importance for survival on the earth.

Warming Right Up *(cont.)*

Record the temperature of each soda bottle for each of the times designated.

Predictions: _____

Start	Open Soda Bottle	Soda Bottle with Plastic Wrap
:30		
1:00		
1:30		
2:00		
2:30		
3:00		
3:30		
4:00		
4:30		
5:00		
5:30		
6:00		
6:30		
7:00		
7:30		
8:00		
8:30		
9:00		
9:30		
10:00		
30:00		
60:00		

Warming Right Up *(cont.)*

Make a point graph of your results and then answer the questions.

Use two different colors to graph your results: one, for the soda bottle that had plastic wrap, the other color for the open soda bottle. This will make it easier to compare your results.

Questions:

1. What was the warmest temperature achieved in the . . .

   Covered soda bottle? _____

   Open soda bottle?_____

2. At what time did the bottle reach its warmest temperature in the . . .

   Covered soda bottle? _____

   Open soda bottle?_____

3. During the first ten minutes, from what two time periods was there the greatest increase?

   Covered soda bottle....from_____ to _____

   Open soda bottle......from_____ to _____

4. How did your predictions compare to your results? _____

5. How can you explain the results?_____

   _____

   _____

Heating Up the Planet

Question

What is global warming?

Setting the Stage

- Review with students the greenhouse effect.
- Set up the following demonstration for your students to observe. This will help them to start thinking about gases.
- Pour 1 cup (250 mL) of vinegar into a wine bottle. Light a candle.
- Pour baking soda into the vinegar. "Pour" the gas that is formed by the reaction of vinegar and baking soda over the burning candle. Do not pour out the liquid. The candle will go out because the carbon dioxide produced from the reaction will push away the oxygen which is needed for the candle to stay burning.
- Use small groups to brainstorm theories about what caused the candle to go out. Each group should share its theory.
- Once your class has had adequate time to discuss the outcome, repeat the demonstration and explain it as it as happening.

Materials Needed for Entire Class

- vinegar
- juice bottles
- matches
- bromothymol blue (BTB)
- drinking straw
- poster board
- baking soda
- candle
- 2 cups per student...clear cup, beaker
- measuring cup
- small and large round balloons
- copy of Global Warming Statistics (page 58), one per student

Note to the teacher: In this set of tests, students repeat the same procedure three times. BTB is an indicator for the presence of carbon dioxide, CO_2. If global warming is attributed to an increased level of carbon dioxide, scientists need to be able to test for the presence of CO_2. By mixing CO_2 and BTB, one can roughly determine the concentrations of CO_2.

Procedure

1. Demonstrate:
   - Pour 1/2 cup (125 mL) of vinegar into a wine or juice bottle.
   - Pour 1/3 cup (83 g) of baking soda into a small round balloon.
   - Attach the balloon to the top of the bottle.
   - Tip the balloon up so the baking soda pours into the vinegar.
   - Observe. (The balloon will fill up with CO_2 gas.)
   - Twist the balloon shut so gas cannot escape.
   - Put a straw into the balloon, allowing little CO_2 to escape.
   - Pour 1/2 cup (125 mL) of BTB into a clear container.

Heating Up the Planet *(cont.)*

Procedure *(cont.)*

- Place the straw into the BTB solution.
- Allow the gas from the balloon to be released through the straw into the BTB solution.
- What happened? There should be a color change.
- The CO_2 concentration levels change in color. Those with the least amount of CO_2 are bluish, a little more concentrated turns a greenish, and the most concentrated are yellowish green and yellow.

2. Ask your class to explain what happened.
   - BTB tests for the presence of CO_2.
   - Vinegar and baking soda combine to form CO_2.
   - Add the gas from vinegar and baking soda to BTB and it changes color indicating a presence of CO_2.

3. Ask your class what gas they exhale.
   - How could they test to see if the CO_2 they exhale is more or less concentrated than the gas made by the reaction of vinegar and baking soda? Give each student a straw and a cup with 1/3 cup (83 mL) of BTB. What type of procedure can they devise to test CO_2 levels?
   - Adapted from activities from GEMS (Great Explorations in Math and Science): *Global Warming and the Greenhouse Effect.* Lawrence Hall of Science, University of California, 1990.

4. Challenges:
   - Ask students how they can test the CO_2 levels in their classroom.
   - How could we test the CO_2 levels produced by cars?

Extensions

- Have students research global warming effect. Highlight the following vocabulary: *atmosphere, ozone layer, ultraviolet light, greenhouse effect, carbon dioxide, methane, chlorofluorocarbons (CFC), fossil fuel, climate change, nitrous oxides, deforestation.*
- Have students graph and discuss statistics about global warming. (See Global Warming Statistics page 58.)

Closure

Review with students the results for which was most concentrated: vinegar and baking soda or the air we exhale?

Issue Analysis: Global Warming Is a Global Problem

If the global warming theory is true, then there could be terrible consequences. Some people believe we should act immediately to reduce the greenhouse gases to prevent disaster. Some fear the following consequences if the earth is really warming: climate changes, rises in sea level, changes in rainfall patterns effecting ecosystems, increased temperatures impacting human survival. Others believe that more research is needed to prove the theory before countries participate in expensive modifications to transportation and manufacturing systems.

Heating Up the Planet *(cont.)*

Global Warming Statistics

Graph #1— The amount of major greenhouse gases - 1957-1987.
Source: World Resource Institute, 1990.

Year	Billion metric tons of carbon equivalents.
1957	2
1967	3 1/4
1977	5
1987	6

Graph #2— Sources of Carbon Dioxide in the United States, 1987.
Source: World Resource Institute, 1990.

Sources	In percentages:
Electric Utilities:	33
Industry:	24
Residential and Commercial:	11
Transportation:	31

Graph #3— Changes in Carbon Dioxide Concentration in the Atmosphere.
Source: World Resources Institute.

Year	CO_2 levels measured in estimated parts per million.
1775	280
1825	285
1875	290
1925	300
1975	355

Graph #4— Per Capita Greenhouse Gas Emissions, by Country, 1988.
Source: World Resources Institute, 1991.

Country	Measured in tons of carbon per capita.
USA:	5.5
Canada:	5
Netherlands:	3
France:	2.4
Spain:	2.3
Australia:	5
United Kingdom:	3.8
Italy:	2.5
Japan:	2.4

Let's Reduce Carbon Dioxide Levels

Question

How can I help reduce the amount of CO_2 I am putting into the atmosphere?

Setting the Stage

- Review with students the sources of CO_2.
- Have students brainstorm a list of ways people produce CO_2.
- Ask students to trace the source of CO_2. (For example, turning on a light bulb will produce CO_2 if oil is burned to produce the electricity.)
- Record the list and sources on a chart in your classroom.
- Sources of CO_2: driving a car, turning on a light bulb, using hot water, turning on the heat, turning on the air conditioner, using a newspaper, drinking a soda from an aluminum can, washing clothes, taking a shower/bath.

Materials Needed for Each Individual

- poster board
- colored markers or crayons
- copy of Reduction statistics (page 60)
- copy of Reduction Plan Form (page 61)

Procedure

1. Assign each student one item from the class list on ways that people produce CO_2. Have them complete a Reduction Plan Form (page 61).
2. As a group, read through each reduction plan. Add other ideas from your class.
3. Using the ideas from their reduction plans, have students design posters that explain the following:
   - The source of CO_2.
   - Steps for Reducing CO_2.
   - Actual pounds of CO_2 saved. (Refer to page 60.)
4. Have students display their posters around your room.

Extensions

- Invite a representative from your local energy company to speak to your class about conservation strategies.
- Have students research the gas mileage efficiency levels of different models of cars. Discuss with students why certain models are popular.
- Have students calculate the gas mileage of family car or school vehicle.

Closure

- Have students spend time looking at all the posters.
- In their environmental issues journals, have students describe 3–5 actions they can regularly practice to reduce the amount of CO_2 they produce.

Let's Reduce Carbon Dioxide Levels *(cont.)*

Reduction Statistics

Source: "Beat the Heat: The CO_2 Challenge." *Children's Earth Fund*, Fall, 1991. Scholastic Inc. Publication.

You and your family can reduce the amount of carbon dioxide you put into the atmosphere by following some of these energy saving practices. The amount of CO_2 saved is listed in pounds and kilograms (kg).

Activity	Pounds (kg) Saved/Year
Tune-up your car annually.	900 (405 kg)
Combine car errands into one trip.	500 (225 kg)
Keep car tires properly inflated.	250 (112.5 kg)
Trade in a gas guzzler for a car that gets 5 miles more per gallon.	2000 (900 kg)
Turn out lights when we leave.	120 lbs/room (54 kg)
Set thermostat one degree lower this winter.	410 (electric) (184.5 kg)
Turn thermostat 10 degrees lower at night.	2070 (electric) (931.5 kg) 1260 (oil) (567 kg)
Get low flow shower heads.	920 (electric) (414 kg) 560 (oil) (252 kg)
Plant a tree on the south or west side of your home to provide cooling inside.	150 (67.5 kg)
Recycle one aluminum can a day.	140 (63 kg)
Recycle one glass bottle a day.	100 (45 kg)
Recycle one newspaper a day.	50 (22.5 kg)

Let's Reduce Carbon Dioxide Levels *(cont.)*

Reduction Plan Form

Use the details from page 60 and plan out a strategy for reducing the amount of CO_2 that you and your family contribute to the atmosphere.

Try to reduce your CO_2 levels by 2,000 lbs (900 kg).

List your plan below.

Activity	Pounds (kg) Saved/Year
Total Reduction:	

Just the Facts

We all use water everyday. How many ways have you used water this week? Our water is recycled over and over again; there is never any new water produced. Because there is no new water, we have to be very careful about how we use our water and what we add to it.

Key Words

Water Cycle—the water in the world is reused over and over again through the processes of evaporation, transpiration, condensation, precipitation, and runoff.

Water Consumption—the amount of water we use through domestic and commercial use.

Groundwater—the water that is kept underground; it is often filtered and cleaned as it percolates through the soil and rocks. We rely on groundwater for drinking water and often times, irrigation.

Water Conservation—reducing the amount of water we use, thus keeping more fresh water accessible for a variety of uses.

Make a list of all the ways people use water.

1. _____   7. _____

2. _____   8. _____

3. _____   9. _____

4. _____   10. _____

5. _____   11. _____

6. _____   12. _____

Your Water and My Water

Question

What happens to the water in the water cycle?

Setting the Stage

- Write the following words on the board: *evaporation, condensation, transpiration, precipitation, groundwater*, and *run-off*.
- Ask each student to draw a picture of the water cycle and label the parts of the cycle using the words on the board.

Materials Needed for Each Group

- three jars
- sand
- 12" x 12" (30 cm x 30 cm) piece of screen
- food coloring: red or orange
- ruler
- potting soil
- soil from school yard
- beaker or measuring cup
- water
- clock with a second hand
- copy of Water Model Directions (page 64), one per student
- data-capture sheets (pages 65-66), one each per student

Procedure

1. Split your class into three groups. Each group will be making a model of the water cycle. Each group will have a different type of soil, but the amount of water added will be the same.
2. Give each student a copy of the Water Model Directions (page 64). Be sure to assign a certain type of soil and have the groups write their soil type on their directions sheet. Once the models are completed, bring them all together to make predictions.

   Have them record their predictions on the base of the directions sheet.
3. From this point, all students must pour the water onto their models at the exact same time and then record observations at regular intervals. Although students have mixed up 6.5 oz (200 mL) of colored water, only 5 oz (150 mL) should be poured on the model. The remaining 1.7 oz (50 mL) can be used for color comparison in the analysis of the model. It will be best if one student pours the water, another student watches the clock, and the other students record observations. Observations should be recorded on their first data-capture sheet (page 65) and then questions answered on their second data-capture sheet (page 66).

Extensions

- Have students try to determine how much water in the world is actually usable.
- Have someone from your local water district talk to your class about water consumption.
- Take your class to a local water treatment facility to watch the cleaning process of our usable water.

Closure

In their environmental issues journals, have students write about the importance of the water cycle.

Your Water and My Water *(cont.)*

Water Model Directions

Materials Needed

- large container
- soil your group will be using
- piece of screen
- ruler
- beaker
- food coloring
- rocks

READ ALL THE DIRECTIONS BEFORE BEGINNING TO BUILD YOUR MODEL.

Procedure *(Student Instructions)*

1. Roll the screen into a tube with a diameter of about 2" (5 cm). This will represent a well.
2. Place the tube into the container vertically. One person will need to hold the tube in place while the others continue building the model.
3. Gently cover the bottom of the container with the small rocks so that the rocks are about 2" (5 cm) deep.
4. Pour enough water into the model so that the water level is about 3/4" (2 cm) deep. This will represent groundwater.
5. Pour on enough of your soil so that it is 8" (10 cm) deep.
6. Release your screen tube. At this point the rocks and soil should be surrounding the tube and holding it in place.
7. Fill your beaker with 6.5 oz (200 mL) of water. Add five drops of red food coloring. Swirl to mix. DO NOT ADD THIS WATER. This will represent your "polluted" water.
8. Draw a picture of your model on the back of this page.
9. Bring your model to the front of the classroom with the other models to display.

During the next step, each group will be pouring 5 oz (150 mL) of red water on their model. What do you think will happen? Write your prediction below for each model:

Sand _____

_____

School Soil _____

_____

Potting Soil_____

_____

64

Your Water and My Water *(cont.)*

You will need to record observations from the time you pour your colored water on until the end of this sheet. Write specific details about depth of water from the soil surface, color of "groundwater," changes in the "well." Remember: Only pour 5 oz (150 mL) of your water; you need 1.7 oz (50 mL) left over to compare the color changes.

Start: Pour in 5 oz (150 mL) on the model. **DO NOT POUR ANY WATER DOWN THE WELL.**

Start	Depth from Surface	Color of Groundwater	Changes in the Well	Other
15 sec.				
30 sec.				
1:00				
1:30				
2:00				
2:30				
3:00				
3:30				
4:00				
4:30				
5:00				
7:00				
9:00				
12:00				
15:00				
30:00				
60:00				

Your Water and My Water

Answer the questions.

1. At what time was the "polluted" water seen in the groundwater?

    _____

2. At what time was the "polluted water" seen in the well?

    _____

3. When did you notice the biggest changes in your model?

    _____

4. At what time did the changes start slowing down?

    _____

5. How could you have changed this model to make the water infiltrate faster into the soil?

    _____

6. How could you have changed this model to make the water stay in the soil longer and not contaminate the groundwater?

    _____

7. How did the color of the water in the model compare to your leftover 1.7 oz (50 mL) of "polluted" water? What were the changes? If there were changes, why do you suppose there were changes?

    _____

8. What does this model show you about the relationship of water pollution above ground and in the groundwater?

    _____

9. If you lived on this land, how would your drinking water have been affected?

    _____

Our Water and Our Responsibility

Question

What can I do to help prevent water pollution?

Setting the Stage

- Have students list as many ways as possible that people use water. Next to each way, list anything that might be added to the water. For example: SHOWER—shampoo, soap.
- Have students identify those items on the list that could be harmful to plants and animals.
- Discuss with students where the water in their home goes after it goes to the drain (sewage treatment plant or septic tank).

Pre Assignment For Water Analysis:

1. Find the water meter in your home or school.
2. Record the water reading on a Monday morning and then record it again in five days, on Friday morning. Calculate the amount of water that was used.

   This amount should be recorded on your Water Conservation Proposal (page 70).

Materials Needed for Each Individual

- calculator
- graph paper
- copy of Water Use Chart (page 69)
- copy of Water Conservation Proposal (page 70)

  Note to the teacher: Each student will make a plan for water conservation. They will outline their plans, implement them, evaluate their success, and make recommendations for further changes.

Procedure

1. Give each student a copy of the Water Use Chart (page 69). After each item is a column to be filled in with suggestions for ways of reducing the amount of water used. Have students complete their charts.
2. Discuss with students the results as a class. Focus on some of the implications of the suggestions for water conservation. For example, if a student suggests not taking a shower everyday...what might the implications be for this?
3. Listed below are some suggestions for conservation.
   - During a shower: wet down, soap up, rinse...save 4 gallons (15 L).
   - Take a shower instead of a bath.
   - Flush toilet less frequently.
   - Place a half gallon (1.89 L) milk jug in your toilet tank to reduce the amount of water used per flush.
   - Put in low flow showerhead and faucets; they can reduce water use by 50%.
   - Wash cars and water lawns only when absolutely necessary.
   - Water lawn in coolest part of day to reduce evaporation.
   - Fill a sink with water for washing hands, shaving, etc.
   - Turn off water while brushing teeth.

Our Water and Our Responsibility *(cont.)*

Procedure *(cont.)*

4. Once students have evaluated possible ways for conserving water, they are to write up a proposal for their own water conservation plan. They will again be recording their water consumption for a five day period. They will then be able to compare their pre-conservation efforts with their actual conservation usage. Encourage students to get their other family members involved. Each student should fill out a Water Conservation Proposal (page 70) and answer the questions at the end of the week. Discuss with students their results.

Extensions

- Have students draw diagrams of the different types of water treatment, both municipal and home (wells and septic fields).
- Have students research and graph the different uses of water in our country: irrigation, energy, livestock, industry, commercial, and domestic.

Closure

Have students identify areas in the school where water conservation could be implemented. Then, have them develop a series of posters to place near sinks, fountains, showers, etc., to educate other students about water conservation.

Issue Analysis: The Population of the Southwestern United States Continues to Grow.

People are drawn to the area for the sunny, warm weather. However, much of the area they are living in was once desert. Now these same areas have grass and trees because of all the irrigation. One area in particular consumes a great deal of water—golf courses. Some say that so much water has been diverted from the Colorado River to make the southwestern United States habitable that the river no longer has a mouth that empties into the sea, for the water is all used up before it reaches the ocean.

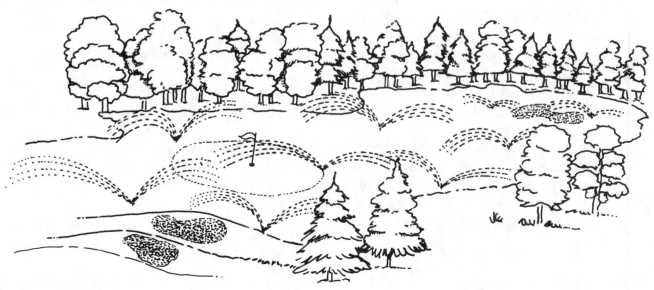

Our Water and
Our Responsibility *(cont.)*

Water Use Chart

Listed below are some common household uses for water and the approximate water consumption for each use.

In the column to the right of the examples, list some suggestions for reducing water consumption for each activity.

Common Household Uses for Water	Water Consumption	How to Reduce Water Consumption
Shower	25 gallons (94.5 L)	
Full Bath	36 gallons (136 L)	
Toilet Flushing	6–7 gallons (19–26.5 L)	
Washing Hands	2 gallons (7.5 L)	
Shaving (tap running)	20 gallons (75.5 L)	
Brushing teeth (tap running)	10 gallons (38 L)	
Wash Car	45–50 gallons (170–189 L)	
Water Lawn/Garden	65–80 gallons (246–302 L)	
Dishwasher	40–50 gallons (151–189 L)	
Clothes Washer	35–40 gallons (132–151 L)	

Our Water and
Our Responsibility (cont.)

Water Conservation Proposal

My water consumption for one week was_____ gallons.

My proposal for conserving water over the next week will be to do the following things:

1. _____

2. _____

3. _____

4. _____

5. _____

Your water meter reading on Monday morning when you wake up. _____

Your water meter reading again on Friday morning when you wake up. _____

Calculate the usage for the five days: _____gallons.

Answer the questions below after your water conservation week.

1. How many gallons did you save by your conservation plan? _____

2. List any difficulties you had implementing your plan _____

   _____

3. Of the things you did, which were easy to remember? _____

   Which were hard to remember to do? _____

4. How did other household members get involved in your conservation? Did your efforts make them more aware? _____

5. Why do you think that water conservation plans are not used by everybody?

   _____

Just the Facts

Think of all the ways people use the land all around the world. We use the land to build our homes on, to grow our food on, to grow trees that we harvest for products we need. We use the water that flows over the land for drinking and irrigating, and we dig for minerals that we need. We also use the land for highways, cities, schools, industry, and power production. In addition, we use the land for recreation—parks, trails for hiking and biking, ski resorts, and beaches.

We use the land in many ways. Some of the uses do not harm the earth's ecosystems, but some of our actions are very damaging. What are some land uses that might disrupt an ecosystem?

How many people do you think are using this land? What is the world's population?

Consider these facts:

- The world population is about 5.2 billion and growing by about 90 million each year. By the year 2025, the estimated world population will reach 10 billion. More than 90% of this projected growth will take place in the developing nations of Africa, Asia, and Latin America. These countries could very well double their populations in 33 years.

- Countries with rapid population growth often rank low in the quality of life and high in human suffering. Rapid growth is often accompanied by environmental destruction.

- In many countries, birth rates exceed death rates so the populations continue to grow. There are very few countries with zero population growth where the death rates and birth rates are equal.

- How will this population growth impact our ecosystems? What demands will be placed on our land for food production and space for housing and even recreation?

- There are many issues surrounding population growth and land use. There are many opinions that are based on a variety of beliefs and values that need to be explored and respected. But with all the different opinions, how can we make decisions that do not permanently harm the world's ecosystems?

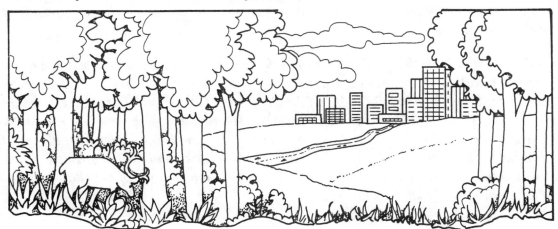

To Ski or Not To Ski

Question

What are the issues involved in land development?

Setting the Stage

(This is a true scenario based on a research project supported by Canadian Parks and Earthwatch. The investigator is Jenny Feick, and the author of this book worked with Ms. Feick during the summer of 1993 to survey the people about their feelings toward the development of their community.)

Read the following text to your students.

Nestled along the Columbia River in southern British Columbia is a small town of 5,000 people. This town of Revelstoke has survived many economic, environmental, and social challenges. The people of Revelstoke are an independent, strong willed group. They have made their lives in this town despite its isolation due to huge mountains and severe winters. They have found ways to support themselves based on the needs of other Canadians.

They have worked on the Canadian Railroad, the Trans-Canadian Highway, the hydroelectric dams on the Columbia River, and in the timber industry. The people of Revelstoke are survivors. They have ridden an economic roller coaster as the projects have come and gone in their community. Everyone had solid incomes while the dam was being built or the road constructed, but once the projects were finished, their incomes were also finished. In fact, most needed to find entirely new ways of supporting themselves. Their incomes have not been predictable or stable.

However, one thing has been predictable, and that is their commitment to their community and each other. They care deeply about their environment and fought hard to protect their air, water, and open space. They are surrounded by some of the most spectacular wilderness areas and mountains in the world. Everyone admires and appreciates the beauty.

The people work hard to maintain a cohesive, caring community. They work together to solve their problems and are united on issues that threaten their well being.

Unfortunately, they have been haunted by plagues that are often associated with unemployment and low incomes: alcohol and drug abuse, family problems, poor educational opportunities, physical abuse.

One of the most impressive things about the area is the mountains. Sitting in the town of Revelstoke is a small ski resort, Mount MacKenzie. It has been run by the town on a very small scale. However, it has the potential to be a first class, world ski resort. In fact, if the mountain were fully developed, it would have the sixth greatest elevation difference in the world for ski hills. Development of the ski hill would put Revelstoke on the map and bring skiers from all over the world. It would also dramatically change the town of Revelstoke and the community. Some of the changes would be very positive for social and economic reasons. Some of the changes could be negative for environmental and social reasons.

To Ski or Not To Ski *(cont.)*

Materials Needed for Entire Class

- video camera (optional)
- overhead projector

Materials Needed for Each Group

- poster board
- colored markers or crayons
- map of Canada
- map of North America
- copy of Players in Mt. MacKenzie (page 74), one per student
- copy of Simulation Directions (page 75), one per student
- copy of City Council Score Sheet (page 76)

Procedure

1. Using the maps, have students locate the following places:
   Canada, United States, British Columbia, Washington, Idaho, Montana, Calgary, Vancouver, Revelstoke, (found in the southern part of British Columbia about half-way between Vancouver and Calgary), Banff National Park, Columbia River (trace the mouth and source), Rocky Mountains, Columbia Mountains.
2. Then have students make a list of possible players in the Mount MacKenzie issue and list their possible positions.
3. Next have students read over the players (page 74) and Simulation Directions (page 75).
4. Assign students to their groups. It is easiest if it is a random assignment so students have to think about the possibilities rather than just advocate a position they already agree with.
5. Give students 2-3 days to prepare for the hearing.
6. Hold the hearing in a room where students can be easily heard and seen.
7. After the hearing, have students total up the scores on their City Council Score Sheets (page 76). These scores will help determine the future of the ski resort.

Extensions

- Invite a land developer to speak to your class about the steps required to develop a tract of land.
- Have students survey newspapers and magazines for articles on land use and development. Who are the players and what are their positions?
- Focus on a local land use conflict. Invite speakers from the conflicting groups to state their cases to your class. Have students evaluate the issue from as many different perspectives as possible.
- Have students survey people on a land use issue.

Closure

Review with students all of the presentations. Then, in their environmental issues journals, have students write their own opinions about the development of the mountain.

To Ski or Not To Ski *(cont.)*

The Players In Mount MacKenzie

You will be representing one of the following groups in a hearing to decide the future of Mount MacKenzie.

1. **Economic Development Commission**

   Concerned about the economic stability of Revelstoke.

   Concerned about business success. They work with new business to help them get established in the community.

2. **Friends of Mount Revelstoke and Glacier**

   Nonprofit organization that is concerned about the future of the two parks that border Revelstoke. They are interested in preserving habitat and species of the park.

3. **North Columbia Resource Council**

   Mainly a group focused on the timber industry. Forestry is big business in British Columbia, and trees are money. They are concerned with managing the trees so that the forests will continue to supply the timber industry. They are a conservation group advocating wise use of timber.

4. **Revelstoke Community Vision Committee**

   A group writing a vision for the community. The vision incorporates balancing the economic needs of the town along with the social and environmental concerns. There are people on the committee from businesses, schools, health concerns, environmental groups, and city government.

5. **Revelstoke Environment Action Committee**

   Concerned about addressing environmental issues that threaten the environment of Revelstoke. One issue they recently battled was preserving the mountain water of Revelstoke for drinking water by not adding chlorine, as the Canadian government had ruled a town their size was required to do.

6. **Canadian Parks Service**

   A national government organization concerned about the impact that changes on any part of the ecosystem might have on the parks. Although the borders of the park are outlined on maps, the animals come and go into the park; therefore, the Canadian Parks Service feels that development needs to be watched and monitored.

7. **Revelstoke Tourism Division**

   They help tourists visiting the area and try to attract new visitors to Revelstoke. They advertise and support events in the town that would attract tourists. Tourists are a definite potential source of income since so many people travel to the surrounding national parks and Calgary and Vancouver. To get to those two cities, many drivers pass right through Revelstoke.

To Ski or Not To Ski *(cont.)*

Simulation Directions

You will be participating in a town meeting regarding the development of Mount MacKenzie. The ski hill is currently owned by the city of Revelstoke, but it is for sale. There are developers from all over the world considering investing in the ski mountain and making it a world class ski resort.

You are going to be representing one of the groups at the town meeting. Your job is to develop a persuasive presentation that will outline your group's position on the development of the ski resort.

You will also need to be prepared to answer clarifying questions by the city council members who will be deciding the future of the ski resort based on your presentations.

Over the next few days, you will need to prepare the following:

1. A five–eight minute presentation where everyone in your group speaks. You should explain...
    - what you want to happen—development or no development.
    - why you hold that position.
    - how people in your group will be effected by development.
2. Visual aids that will enhance your presentation and further clarify your position.
3. Characters to role-play individuals who might be members of your group. Each of you will need to adopt a role.
4. An opening statement.
5. A closing statement.

Be Creative! Be Prepared! Practice Your Presentation!

At the town hearing you will be given a score for your presentations based on the following:

- opening statement
- organization
- clarity of presentation and arguments
- visual aid quality
- visual aid effectiveness
- participation by everyone in the group
- answers to questions
- closing statement

The city council members will base their decision for development or against development on the points earned by each group.

Good Luck!

To Ski or Not To Ski *(cont.)*

City Council Score Sheet

Give each group a score of 1–10 for each category. Ten is the best score.

Name of group_____

Opening Statement _____

Organization_____

Clarity and Persuasiveness of Presentation_____

Visual Aid Quality_____

Visual Aid Effectiveness_____

Full Group Participation _____

Responses to Questions _____

Closing Statement _____

Total_____

76

People, People, Everywhere

Question

What is the impact of overpopulation on the environment?

Setting the Stage

- Read the following quote from a letter, put out by Zero Population Growth, 1400 16th Street NW, Washington, DC 20036.

  In the seconds it takes you to read this sentence, 24 people will be added to the Earth's population. Before you've finished this letter, that number will reach 1,000. Within an hour 11,000, By day's end....260,000. Before you go to bed two nights from now, the net growth in human numbers will be enough to fill a city the size of San Francisco. It took four million years for humanity to reach the 2 billion mark. Only 30 years to add a third billion. And now we're increasing by 95 million every single year. No wonder they call it the human race.

- Survey your class for their responses to this letter.
- Have students brainstorm a list of possible environmental issues that might be associated with this type of population growth. Post the list.
- Read your class this quote from the same letter:

  No matter what your cause—it's a lost cause—if we don't come to grips with overpopulation.

- Ask students to fill out the Population Response sheet (page 79) and then discuss their answers.

Materials Needed for Entire Class

- cardboard or plastic chips, ten chips per individual
- candy or stickers
- rules poster
- bell
- copy of Population Response sheet (page 79), one per student
- copy of Issue/Population Analysis sheet (page 80), one per student

Procedure

1. Define for your class renewable versus nonrenewable resources. List examples. Then ask students what types of nonrenewable resources we use. What types of renewable resources do we use?
2. Sit your class in a circle on the floor. (This works best with 10-16 students.)
   Count out ten chips for each person in the circle and put them in a container. Put 1/4 of those chips in the middle of the circle. (For 15 students, you would count out 150 chips and put 38 chips in the center.) Each chip symbolizes a renewable resource (such as crops for food).
3. Read to students the following rules from a poster you have made in advance.
   These chips are a renewable resource.
   All the chips belong to all of you.

People, People, Everywhere *(cont.)*

Procedure *(cont.)*

This game will have 15-second rounds. A bell will ring at the end of each round.

At the end of each round, the number of chips in the pool will double. However, there will never be more chips than the number of chips we counted out at the beginning of the game.

You may not talk during the game.

You may trade in ten chips for a piece of candy (sticker).

4. Have students begin the game. Double the remaining chips each time. If all the chips are depleted, ask everyone to return the chips and start again with the same number of chips. Continue to repeat the game. Eventually, some students will begin to realize that if they all just wait, the chips will double quickly and everyone will get a piece of candy. Enforce the no talking rule and see if they can resolve the depletion of the "resources," chips.

5. If no progress is made, discuss strategies with your class for ensuring a more equitable distribution of the chips. Allow students to discuss ways to overcome the "shortage" problem.

6. Have students play until everyone has received one piece of candy.

7. Discuss with students the outcome of the game.

   • How did people who got all the chips feel?

   • How did people who could not get any chips feel?

   • How did talking about the problem help resolve the inequities?

   • Have you experienced a similar situation at home or school—where there was not enough to go around or some got a lot and others (maybe you) got none?

   • How does this game relate to natural resources and people?

   • How does this game relate to wealthy countries? Developing countries?

Extensions

   • Have students research the birth and death rates of different countries around the world.

   • Have students map the countries that have population growth and zero population growth.

   • Invite a local relief organization to speak to your class about population growth as it relates to starvation, disasters caused by weather, volcanoes, earthquakes, wars, etc.

   • Suggested groups: Red Cross, United Way, CARE, OXFAM, Zero Population Growth, American Friends Service Committee.

Closure

Have students complete their Issue/Population Analysis sheet and add them to their environmental issues journals. Complete the first one together. Then discuss with students the results of each person's analysis.

Issue Analysis: One in Five People Worldwide are Hungry.

60,000 people die of hunger each day. 15% of the world's population consumes 70% of the world's grain supply (either directly or indirectly by feeding livestock).

People, People, Everywhere *(cont.)*

Population Responses

Read the following quote from Zero Population Growth. Respond in complete sentences to the three quotations that follow the quotation.

ZPG..."No matter what your cause—it's a lost cause—if we don't come to grips with overpopulation."

1. What does the above quote mean?

   _____

   _____

   _____

   _____

   _____

2. What are the causes that might be lost causes if overpopulation is not addressed?

   _____

   _____

   _____

   _____

   _____

3. What is one way overpopulation might be controlled?

   _____

   _____

   _____

   _____

   _____

People, People, Everywhere *(cont.)*

Issue/Population Analysis

Listed below are four population growth issues. After each issue, list the possible associated environmental problems. In the next column, list the possible solutions to the environmental problems.

Issue	Environmental Problem	Solution Ideas
High birth rate in an area that has a desert-like climate.		
High birth rate, high infant mortality rate in an area where the soil has been stripped of the nutrients because of over-farming.		
High birth rate, low death rate in a culture dominated by a religion that does not believe in population control. Area is very urban, no farm land.		
Zero population growth rate but a high concentration of people in a small area. Little land left for farming.		

Science Safety

Discuss the necessity for science safety rules. Reinforce the rules on this page or adapt them to meet the needs of your classroom. You may wish to reproduce the rules for each student or post them in the classroom.

1. Begin science activities only after all directions have been given.

2. Never put anything in your mouth unless it is required by the science experience.

3. Always wear safety goggles when participating in any lab experience.

4. Dispose of waste and recyclables in proper containers.

5. Follow classroom rules of behavior while participating in science experiences.

6. Review your basic class safety rules every time you conduct a science experience.

You can still have fun and be safe at the same time!

Environmental Issues Journal

Environmental Issues Journals are an effective way to integrate science and language arts. Students are to record their observations, thoughts, and questions about past science experiences in a journal to be kept in the science area. The observations may be recorded in sentences or sketches which keep track of changes both in the science item or in the thoughts and discussions of the students.

Environmental Issues Journal entries can be completed as a team effort or an individual activity. Be sure to model the making and recording of observations several times when introducing the journals to the science area.

Use the student recordings in the Environmental Issues Journal as a focus for class science discussions. You should lead these discussions and guide students with probing questions, but it is usually not necessary for you to give any explanation. Students come to accurate conclusions as a result of classmates' comments and your questioning. Environmental Issues Journals can also become part of the students' portfolios and overall assessment program. Journals are a valuable assessment tool for parent and student conferences as well.

How To Make a Environmental Issues Journal

1. Cut two pieces of 8 ½" x 11" (22 cm x 28 cm) construction paper to create a cover. Reproduce page 83 and glue it to the front cover of the journal. Allow students to draw environmental issues pictures in the box on the cover.
2. Insert several Environmental Issues Journal pages. (See page 84.)
3. Staple together and cover stapled edge with book tape.

My
Environmental Issues
Journal

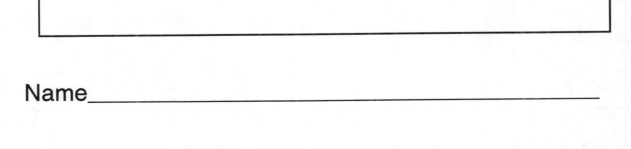

Name_____

Environmental Issues Journal

Illustration

This is what happened:

_____

_____

_____

_____

This is what I learned:

_____

_____

_____

_____

My Science Activity

K-W-L Strategy

Answer each question about the topic you have chosen.

Topic:_____

K - What I Already **Know:** _____

_____

_____

_____

_____

W - What I **Want to Find Out:**_____

_____

_____

_____

_____

L - What I **Learned after Doing the Activity:** _____

_____

_____

_____

_____

Investigation Planner *(Option 1)*

Observation

_____

_____

Question

_____

_____

Hypothesis

_____

_____

Procedure

Materials Needed:

_____

_____

_____

Step-by-Step Directions: (Number each step!)

_____

_____

_____

_____

_____

Investigation Planner *(Option 2)*

Science Experience Form

Scientist _____

Title of Activity _____

Observation: What caused us to ask the question?

_____

_____

_____

Question: What do we want to find out?

_____

_____

_____

Hypothesis: What do we think we will find out?

_____

_____

_____

Procedure: How will we find out? (List step-by-step.)

1. _____

2. _____

3. _____

4. _____

Results: What actually happened?

_____

_____

_____

Conclusions: What did we learn?

_____

_____

_____

Environmental Issues Observation Area

In addition to station-to-station activities, students should be given other opportunities for real-life science experiences. For example, displays of recyclable materials and information about environmental problems can provide vehicles for discovery learning if students are given time and space to observe them.

Set up a environmental issues observation area in your classroom. As children visit this area during open work time, expect to hear stimulating conversations and questions among them. Encourage their curiosity but respect their independence!

Books with facts pertinent to the subject, item, or process being observed should be provided for students who are ready to research more sophisticated information.

Sometimes it is very stimulating to set up a science experience or add something interesting to the Environmental Issues Observation Area without a comment from you at all! If the experiment or materials in the observation area should not be disturbed, reinforce with students the need to observe without touching or picking up.

Assessment Form

The following chart can be used by the teacher to rate cooperative-learning groups in a variety of settings.

Science Groups Evaluation Sheet

Room: _____   Date: _____

Activity: _____

Everyone

. . . gets started.

. . . participates.

. . . knows jobs.

. . . solves group problems.

. . . cooperates.

. . . keeps noise down.

. . . encourages others.

Group									
1	2	3	4	5	6	7	8	9	10

Teacher comment

_____

Bragging rights for the group session: _____

_____

Assessment Form *(cont.)*

The evaluation form below provides student groups with the opportunity to evaluate the group's overall success.

Cooperative Group Evaluation

Assignment: _____

Date: _____

Scientists	Jobs
_____	_____
_____	_____
_____	_____
_____	_____

As a group, decide which face you should fill in and complete the remaining sentences.

1. We finished our assignment on time, and we did a good job.

2. We encouraged each other, and we cooperated with each other.

3. We did best at _____

_____ .

4. Next time we could improve at _____

_____ .

Assessment Form *(cont.)*

The following form may be used as part of the assessment process for hands-on science experiences.

Science Anecdotal Record Form

Date: _____

Scientist's Name: _____

Topic: _____

Assessment Situation: _____

Instructional Task: _____

Behavior/Skill Observed: _____

_____

_____

_____

_____

_____

_____

This behavior/skill is important because _____

_____

_____

_____

_____

_____

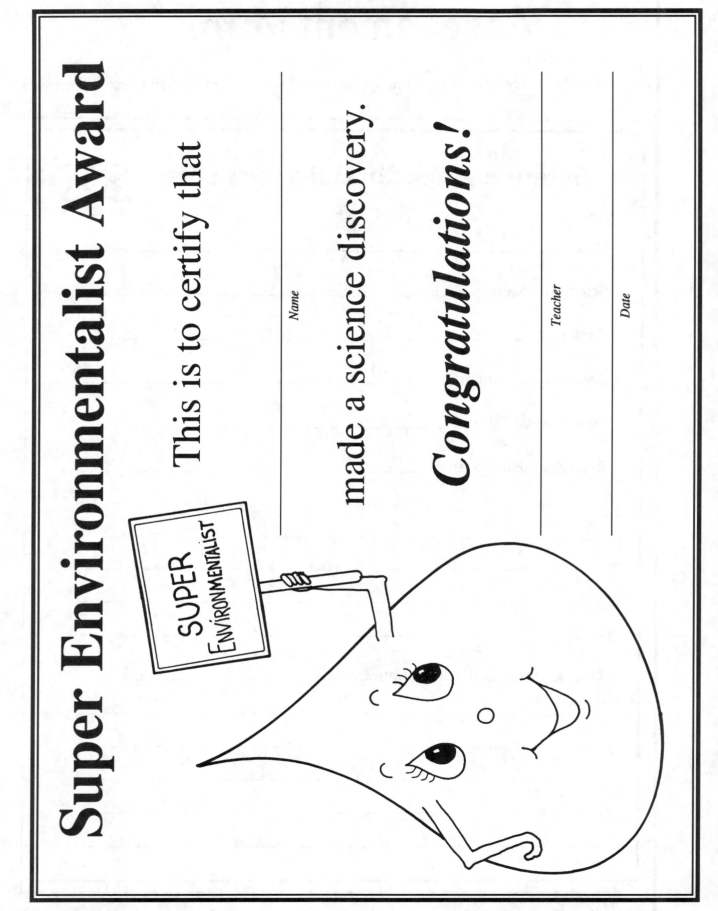

Super Environmentalist Award

This is to certify that

_____

Name

made a science discovery.

Congratulations!

_____

Teacher

_____

Date

SUPER ENVIRONMENTALIST

Glossary

Acid—a solution with a pH from 0–6.9.

Acid Rain—rain that has a high concentration of sulfuric acid and nitric acids due to air pollution.

Base—a solution with a pH from 7.1–14.

Biodegrade—to break down, especially by bacterial action.

Biodiversity—the great variety and range of plants and animals.

Botanist—a person who studies the science of plants.

Conclusion—the outcome of an investigation.

Compost—a mixture of decaying leaves, manure, and other nutritive matter, for improving or fertilizing soil.

Conservationist—a person who wants to protect the land, plants, water, and animals but also thinks people should be able to use these resources.

Consumerism—a movement to protect the consumer from unsafe or defectively manufactured products, and to protect the environment from undue harm.

Deforestation—complete destruction of all forests in an entire region.

Ecosystem—a system made up of a group of living organisms and its physical environment, and the relationship between them.

Environmentalist—a person who is concerned with the problems of the environment.

Experiment—a means of proving or disproving a hypothesis.

Global Warming—an overall increase in the earth's temperature which may be caused by reduced numbers of trees and increased levels of carbon dioxide.

Greenhouse Effect—the natural process of holding in the right amount of heat from the sun so that life can survive on earth.

Groundwater—water that lies under the ground in natural reservoirs, such as springs and wells.

Habitat—a place where a plant or animal naturally lives and grows.

Hypothesis (hi-POTH-e-sis)—an educated guess to a question you are trying to answer.

Investigation—an observation of something followed by a systematic inquiry to examine what was originally observed.

Landfill—an enormous hole where garbage is dumped.

Neutral—a solution with a pH of 7.0.

Observation—careful notice or examination of something.

Ozone Layer— a shield of gases that surrounds the earth and protects us from the sun's harmful rays.

Glossary *(cont.)*

pH—a scale used to measure whether things are acids, bases, or neutral.

Precycling—reducing the amount of solid waste before it enters the home.

Preservationist—a person who wants to preserve the plants, animals, and land as close to their original status as possible.

Procedure—the series of steps carried out in an experiment.

Propaganda—any plan or method to spread opinions or beliefs.

Question—a formal way of inquiring about a particular topic.

Rain Forest—tropical woodlands with an annual rainfall of at least 100" (250 cm).

Recycling—processing and treating discarded materials so that they can be used again.

Results—the data collected after an experiment.

Scientific Method—a systematic process of proving or disproving a given question, following an observation. Observation, question, hypothesis, procedure, results, conclusion, and future investigations comprise the scientific method.

Science-Process Skills—the skills needed to think critically. Process skills include observing, communicating, comparing, ordering, categorizing, relating, inferring, and applying.

Smog—a combination of smoke and fog in the air.

Species—a group of animals or plants that have certain permanent characteristics in common and are able to interbreed.

Toxic Substance—a chemical or mixture of chemicals whose manufacture, distribution, use, or disposal may present an unreasonable risk to health of a person and/or the environment.

Variable—the changing factor of an experiment.

Water Cycle—the cycle in which the water in the world is reused over and over again through the processes of evaporation, infiltration, transpiration, condensation, runoff, etc.

Zoologist—a person who studies the science of animals.

Bibliography

Baker, Jeanine. *Where the Forests Meet the Sea.* Greenwillow, 1988.

Barman, C., Rusch, J, and Cooney, T. *Science and Societal Issues: A Guide for Science Teachers.* Iowa State University Press, 1981.

Baylor, Byrd. *Hawk, I'm Your Brother.* Scribner, 1976.

Bouchard, Dave. *The Elders Are Watching.* Eagle Dancer/Raincoast Books, 1990.

Boyle, Doe & Peter Thomas. *Earth Day Every Day.* Soundprints, 1993.

Breiter, Herta. *Pollution.* Raintree Steck-V, 1987.

Bright, Michael. *Polluting the Oceans.* Watts, 1991.

Caduto, Michael & Joseph Bruchac. *Keepers of the Earth: Native American Stories, & Environmental Activities for Children.* Fulcrum Pub.,1988.

Cherry, Lynne. *The Great Kapok Tree.* HBJ, 1990.

Cornell, Joseph. *Sharing the Joy of Nature.* Dawn Publications, 1989.

Cosgrove, Stephen. *Serendipity.* Creative Education, Inc. 1974.

Delton, Judy. *Trash Bash.* Dell, 1992.

Dr. Seuss. *The Lorax.* Random Books, 1971.

The Earth Works Group. *50 Simple Things You Can Do to Save the Earth.* Earthworks Press, 1989.

50 Simple Things Kids Can Do to Save the Earth. Earthworks Press, 1990.

Kids Heroes of the Environment. Earthworks Press, 1990.

Fradin, Dennis. *Earth.* Childrens, 1989.

Gore, Willma. *Earth Day.* Enslow Pubs., 1992.

Hare, Tony. *Recycling.* Watts, 1992.

Hungerford, H., Litherland, R., Peyton, B., Ramsey, J., and Volk, T. *Investigating and Evaluating Environmental Issues* and *Action Skill Development Modules.* Stipes Publishing, 1988.

Jaspersohn, William. *How the Forest Grew.* Greenwillow, 1992

Kalman, Bobbie. *Our Earth.* Crabtree Pub Co., 1987.

Kalman, Bobbie & Janine Schawb. *Air I Breathe.* Crabtree Pub. Co., 1992.

Lambert, David. *Pollution & Conservation.* Watts, 1986.

Leopold, Aldo. *A Sand County Almanac.* Ballantine Books, 1966.

Lepthien Emile & Joan Kalbacken. *Recycling.* Childrens, 1991.

Levine, Shar & Grafton, Allison. *Projects for a Healthy Planet: Simple Environmental Experiments for Kids.* Wiley, 1992.

Madden, Don. *The Wartville Wizard.* Macmillan, 1986.

McVey, Vicki. *Sierra Club Kid's Guide to Planet Care and Repair.* Sierra Club, 1993.

National Wildlife Federation Staff. *The Class Project.* Natl. Wildlife, 1988.

Pollution: Problems & Solutions. Natl. Wildlife, 1991.

Pittman, Helena Clare. *The Gift of the Willows.* Lerner/Carolrhoda, 1988.

Rayburn, Cherie. *Enviro-Man to the Rescue.* Current Inc, 1991.

Romanova, Natalia. *Once There Was a Tree.* Dial Bks Young, 1989.

Bibliography (cont.)

Rothman, Joel. *Once There Was a Stream.* Scroll Press, 1973.

Roy, Ronald. *A Thousand Pails of Water.* Knopf, 1978.

Sheehan, Kathryn & Mary Waidner. *Earth Child.* Coun Oak Bks., 1992.

Snow, Ted. *Global Change.* Childrens, 1990.

Stille, Darlene. *Water Pollution.* Childrens, 1990.

Van Metre, Steve and Weiler, Bill. *The Earth Speaks.* The Earth Institute for Education, 1983.

Wasserman, P. & Doyle, A. *Earth Matters.* Zero Population Growth, Inc., 1991.

Wilcox, Charlotte. *Trash.* Lerner Publications, 1989.

World Resources Institute. *Environmental Almanac.* Houghton Mifflin Company, 1992.

Spanish Titles

Muzik, K. *Dentro del arrecife del coral (At Home in the Coral Reef).* Charlesbridge Publishing, 1992.

Seuss. *El Lorax (The Lorax).* Lectorum, 1993.

Willow, D. *Dentro de la selva tropical (At Home in the Rain Forest).* Charlesbridge Publishing, 1992.

Wright, A. *¿Les echaremos de menos? Especies en peligro de extincion (Will We Miss Them? Species in Danger of Extinction).* Charlesbridge Publishing, 1992.

Technology

Chariot Software. *Eco-Adventures in the Rainforest* and *Eco-Adventures in the Ocean.* Available from CDL Software Shop, (800)637-0047. software

Chris Crawford Games. *Balance of the Planet.* Available from CDL Software Shop, (800)637-0047. software

Cornet/MTI Film & Video. *Amazonia.* Available from Cornet/MTI Film & Video, (800)777-8100. videodisc and video

Earthquest. Earthquest, *EcoQuest I*, and *Earthquest Explores Ecology.* Available from Troll, (800)526-5289. software

Focus Media. *Earth and Environmental Investigations.* Available from CDL Software Shop, (800)637-0047. software

National Geographic Society. *GTV: Planetary Manager* and *STV: Rain Forest.* Available from Sunburst, (800)321-7511. videodisc

Queue. *Tracing Cycles in the Environment: Ecology.* Available from CDL Software Shop, (800)637-0047. software